Hidden
Within Us

Hidden Within Us

A Radical New Understanding of the Mind-Body Connection

SAMUEL J. MANN, MD

Hidden Within Us: A Radical New Understanding of the Mind-Body Connection

For information about this title or to order other books and/or electronic media, contact the publisher:

Samuel J. Mann, MD
isleofmann@aol.com

ISBNs:
979-8-9852023-0-4 (print)
979-8-9852023-1-1 (eBook)

Printed in the United States of America

To my patients, who have been my teachers.

Table of Contents

Introduction

I am a physician, not a psychologist.
 I believe this book could not be written by a psychologist because it requires a physician's experience—as well as noticing an unrecognized phenomenon that became impossible for me to ignore.

It is widely known that the day-to-day stress adults experience can cause physical symptoms including tension headaches, insomnia, fatigue, diarrhea, and more. This stress can also lead to undesirable health habits: overeating, weight gain, substance abuse, and others.

Many also believe that day-to-day stress and emotional distress are a direct cause of chronic medical conditions like hypertension, ulcers, inflammatory bowel disease, and others, and that mind-body interventions are useful in treating or preventing them. However, an enormous amount of mind-body research performed over decades has largely failed to confirm this belief.

My clinical experience agrees with those negative findings. Yet traditional mind-body beliefs persist. In accord with those beliefs, the "psychosocial" history physicians are taught to obtain from patients continues to focus on their *current* day-to-day stress and emotional distress.

So, is there a mind-body connection? The answer is a definite *yes*. Yet what I've observed has led me to a very different understanding of this connection; one that is rarely, if ever, considered or mentioned. It is a perspective with important implications concerning our understanding and treatment of many widespread medical conditions whose cause remains inadequately understood. I wrote this book to convey that understanding and its implications.

I will present this rarely considered yet unavoidable understanding as it unfolded to me. I learned that, to a large extent, the mind-body connection does not reside in the emotions we *feel* and that distress us. I came to realize that an absence of emotional distress does not preclude a mind-body origin. I was surprised to observe the unsuspected involvement of much more powerful emotions that, ironically, we don't feel, and would insist that we don't feel.

Evidence suggests that this connection pertains to a long list of conditions (among them, hypertension, chronic fatigue syndrome, fibromyalgia, other chronic pain syndromes, colitis, autoimmune diseases, migraine, unexplained anxiety, and possibly many others) that are not well explained by medical science. I do not believe that this mind-body origin is operative in all patients with these conditions. The proportion of patients in whom a given condition is attributable to this mind-body understanding differs from condition to condition. Even so, I believe it is an unrecognized cause or contributor in many patients and offers important, yet rarely explored treatment implications.

Patients see physicians for medical problems. Physicians are trained to obtain information about a current illness, review the past medical and surgical history, and inquire about current stress and emotional distress. However, an important component that is often missing is inquiry about past psychosocial history, and particularly childhood.

A classic example of the invisibility of past psychosocial history is apparent in the standard family history we are trained to obtain at every patient's initial visit. We ask the age of the patient's parents. If a parent is deceased, we ask their age at the time of death. Death at an early age is often an important clue to genetic risk, a clue that is highly relevant to the patient's care.

However, we are never trained to ask, and no medical textbook suggests that we ask, a crucial corollary question that seems obvious: How old were *you* when your parent died at that young age? To a child, the death of a parent is a far greater emotional stressor/ trauma than is the day-to-day stress during adulthood that is our focus. But because this event occurred decades earlier, it does not draw the physician's attention.

I found that obtaining the psychosocial history often uncovered a past history of trauma or a period of severe, prolonged stress. And listening to my patients' stories, I was often surprised at how many of them, no matter how rough their story, were doing fine, had experienced no psychological repercussions, and had never felt the need to consult a psychologist. I began to ask patients how they had managed to make it through those rough times. This book is about their answers, and the important implications of those answers.

Listening to patients has convinced me that we are much better endowed to handle severe stress and trauma than we realize. Even though we experience severe emotional distress, we have the capacity to be unaware of truly overwhelming emotion. This capacity is a crucial, yet widely overlooked component of our emotional resilience.

I am in awe of how well-equipped so many of us are, whether we realize it or not, to get through the worst of times. Just as we are born with bodies genetically built to help us survive physically, I'm convinced, based on my patients' stories, that we are also endowed with the means to survive emotionally. It is literally in our DNA.

Evolution had to have built this capacity into us. Given what so many encounter in a lifetime, I don't believe humanity could otherwise have survived. It is astounding that we don't realize we have this capacity or that it is operative.

That said, my experience with patients has also taught me that powerful emotions that we don't feel, aren't aware of, and don't suspect that we harbor within us are also at the heart of the mind-body connection. They contribute to the development of many medical conditions whose cause remains inadequately understood and whose treatment remains a challenge for many. In this manner, our emotional resilience is surprisingly—and perhaps counterintuitively—intertwined with the development, even decades later, of medical illness.

In the coming chapters I will explain how I came to realize the role that our capacity to not feel plays in both our emotional resilience and in the mind-body connection. I will also describe the relevance of this understanding in the treatment of medical conditions whose origin has remained elusive—conditions where a mind-body connection has been suspected but remains unproven, and others where it hasn't even been considered.

I will present cases that will make this understanding clear and unavoidable as well as published evidence that supports this revolutionary understanding. I hope this book will open the door to this new understanding, and with it, to new pathways to treatment, healing, and, importantly, self-healing.

I specialize in the treatment of hypertension (high blood pressure), a medical condition that has been the subject of more mind-body research than perhaps any other. The widespread belief has been that stress and emotional distress can cause hypertension and that stress reduction can alleviate it. Yes, stress and emotional distress can transiently increase anyone's blood pressure. However, decades of mind-body research have failed to confirm that they cause *sustained* hypertension or that stress reduction and relaxation techniques can lead to *sustained* blood pressure lowering.

Ironically, in a book about the mind-body connection, I begin by stating that in the overwhelming majority of patients with relatively ordinary hypertension, the hypertension is not caused by stress and emotional distress and is not a mind-body disorder.

I have found a surprising and unexpected mind-body connection in patients with atypical forms of hypertension, including severe hypertension, unexplained episodic hypertension, or hypertension in relatively young patients. Their stories will make this understanding unavoidable, regardless of whether or not you are one of the over 100 million Americans who have hypertension.

More important, I will present observations and published evidence that suggest that this understanding is relevant to other widespread medical conditions that to this day remain inadequately understood and treated.

To protect patients' anonymity, I have changed personal details, but the essence of their stories is preserved. It is their stories that moved me, and, in fact, compelled me to write this book.

PART I

Noticing a New and Different Mind-Body Connection

Chapter 1

The Failure of Traditional Mind-Body Beliefs

The *traditional understanding* of the mind-body relationship that has dominated popular and research attention is that the stress and emotional distress that we experience are the cause of many medical illnesses. However, decades of psychosomatic research have failed to confirm this understanding. Yes, stress can *indirectly* contribute to illness through its effects on health habits such as overeating, smoking, substance abuse, and others. But, no, research has failed to confirm the belief that stress and emotional distress *directly* cause medical illness.

Two conditions that were almost universally considered to be quintessential mind-body disorders are hypertension and peptic ulcer disease. They have been the subject of psychosomatic research for decades. In this chapter I will summarize the results of that research, which make it clear, that the traditional, widely accepted mind-body "understanding" of these two conditions, and likely that of many other chronic medical conditions, is incorrect.

Hypertension and Stress:
Shattering the Long-standing Mind-Body Myth

Over 100 million Americans have hypertension. It is responsible for more visits to the doctor than any other medical condition. It is well-suited to teach us about the mind-body connection because measurement of blood pressure provides a physiologic telltale of the effect of emotions.

In this context, Susan's story was quite surprising.

Susan, 56, came to me because of borderline hypertension, with systolic blood pressure readings ranging from the 120s to the 140s mmHg. The normal range, still debated, is generally considered to be less than 130, and ideally under 120. I was not ready to start Susan on medication, because if I did, she would likely remain on medication the rest of her life. I decided to defer the decision with periodic monitoring of her blood pressure both in my office and at home.

Two years later, at a routine revisit, still without medication, Susan was clearly very upset. She said her son, 32, had been diagnosed with cancer, which was likely to be fatal. He died a year later. During that year, Susan experienced severe emotional distress. She cried during every office visit. Yet despite having borderline hypertension, her blood pressure didn't budge one millimeter, in my office or at home.

Decades of studies have consistently demonstrated that nearly everyone's blood pressure increases in response to acute laboratory stressors such as mental arithmetic, simulated public speaking, and many others. The blood pressure rises, then quickly falls back to its baseline level.

The magnitude of the emotional distress Susan endured dwarfed by far the emotional distress experienced in those studies. Yet during months of severe stress and anguish, her blood pressure hadn't budged.

I've followed the blood pressure of many patients during periods of severe stress. Though everyone tends to blame hypertension on stress, experience has taught me that stress rarely leads to sustained blood pressure elevation. Blood pressure can transiently rise, but the elevation usually is not persistent.

This consistent observation is in accord with the failure of decades of psychosomatic research to confirm a relationship between hypertension and measured levels of emotional distress, such as anger, anxiety, and depression.[1-4] It is also in accord with the inconclusive results of studies that have sought to prove that emotional distress contributes directly to the development of many other medical conditions.

Decades of research have also revealed that stress reduction techniques do not have persisting blood pressure lowering effects.[1] Biofeedback, progressive muscle relaxation, and stress management training have been found to be ineffective.[5-6] And the results of many studies that claimed effectiveness were questionable. Many were compromised by a lack of utilization of 24-hour blood pressure monitoring; most studies predated that technology.

Over decades, thousands of studies were designed, conducted, and analyzed, not by skeptics but almost entirely by research psychologists who believed strongly that stress and emotional distress could eventually cause a persisting increase in blood pressure and that their interventions could help bring the blood pressure under control. Innumerable studies examined the widely suspected role of emotions such as anger and anxiety. Questionnaires were devised to measure perceived anger and anxiety and then assess its correlation with blood pressure and the development of hypertension.

Despite the widespread expectation of a relationship, none was found, as discussed in numerous reviews. Researchers modified the questionnaires repeatedly; the results did not change. The quality of the studies varied considerably, and, frankly, one can find studies whose results support any and every point of view. But in the aggregate, a significant relationship was not found.

Many studies have examined the role of stress—day-to-day stress, job stress, financial stress, relationship stress, and so on. Yet here as well, the expected relationship was not found.

If stress causes hypertension, one would expect job stress to be a prominent cause, given the amount of time we spend at work and the amount of aggravation we experience. In my review of the topic, most studies failed to find a significant relationship between blood pressure and job stress.[7] Also evident was the limited quality and the cherry-picking of subgroup results in most of the studies that did report a relationship.

The most methodologically sound study in my review measured job stress and 24-hour blood pressure, then reassessed the 24-hour blood pressure five years later.[8] It reported no relationship—not a single millimeter, between job stress and change in blood pressure from its baseline level.

If stress and anxiety don't cause hypertension, why do so many people believe they do? One reason is that stress clearly raises blood pressure in the moment, in almost everyone. This is a normal and necessary physiologic response to acute stress, integral to our "fight or flight reflex." But the effect is not sustained.

Another reason is that many patients feel nervous when a doctor is checking their blood pressure, leading both patient and doctor to believe that anxiety is causing their "hypertension." However, the blood pressure of many of those patients is normal outside the doctor's office. Their anxiety didn't cause hypertension; they didn't *have* hypertension.

Clearly, anxiety can raise blood pressure when it is measured in an office or study setting. The more reliable measurement now regularly used in studies utilizes the 24-hour blood pressure monitor, which measures blood pressure at work, at home, and when asleep. These studies have been less likely to identify any persisting effect of anger, anxiety, or stress on blood pressure.

Thus, decades of studies have led to the current medical consensus that day-to-day stress and emotional distress do not cause hypertension, and that stress reduction techniques are largely ineffective in bringing hypertension under control.

Stomach Ulcers and Stress:
The Death of a Widespread Misconception

In the past, almost everyone viewed stress as the cause of stomach ulcers. I remember a cartoon of an ulcer patient: a man looking harried, spouting drops of sweat in every direction. This almost universally assumed belief turned out to be incorrect.

The dramatic change in the management of ulcers came with the discovery that in most cases, the bacterium *Helicobacter pylori* (H. pylori) was the cause.[9] At the time, the adherence to the stress hypothesis was widely ingrained, and the H. pylori explanation was met with fierce resistance. To prove his point, researcher Dr. Barry Marshall went to the length of ingesting the bacteria, developing an ulcer, and undergoing endoscopy to demonstrate on biopsy both the ulcer and the presence of H. pylori in the ulcer. He then cured the ulcer with antibiotics. Performed in 1984, this remains one of the most dramatic self-experiments in the history of medicine. His body of research earned Marshall and his colleague Dr. Robin Warren a Nobel Prize in 2005.

Since then, abundant evidence has made it clear that H. pylori, and not stress, is the cause in most cases.[10,11] Other widely recognized causes or contributors are the use of NSAIDs—nonsteroidal anti-inflammatory drugs, such as ibuprofen (Motrin), naproxen (Aleve), or aspirin—drinking, and smoking. As Jones concluded in his review: "At present, there is no definitive study proving a causal relationship between psychological stress and the development of ulcer disease."[10]

As is the case with hypertension, stress does not *directly* cause ulcers. Then why did people think it did? Because stress can *indirectly* contribute to ulcers due to its association with smoking, drinking, and increased use of NSAIDs.[10] Also, stress can cause what is called "dyspepsia," a queasy stomach, which is often wrongly assumed to be an ulcer. And just as stress transiently increases blood pressure, it also transiently increases gastric acid secretion.[10] But it does not cause ulcers.

The final nail in the coffin of the stress/ulcer belief lies in the results of treatment studies. With the use of antibiotics directed at H. pylori, the recurrence rate of ulcers is as low as 10 percent.[11] In contrast, even the most ardent advocates of the stress/ulcer belief acknowledge that treatment directed at stress is ineffective.[12]

It is now clear that day-to-day stress and emotional distress are not a direct cause of these two medical disorders that for decades had been considered classic mind-body disorders. These results capsulize why, if we are to understand the relationship between emotions and medical illness, it is incumbent to move on to a new perspective.

References

1. Mann SJ. Psychosomatic research in hypertension: the lack of impact of decades of research and new directions to consider. J Clin Hypertens (Greenwich). 2012 Oct;14(10):657-64. doi: 10.1111/j.1751-7176.2012.00686.x. Epub 2012 Jul 26. PMID: 23031141.

2. Monk M. Psychologic status and hypertension. Am J Epidemiol. 1980 Aug;112(2):200-8. doi: 10.1093/oxfordjournals.aje.a112985. PMID: 7416147.

3. Suls J, Wan CK, Costa PT Jr. Relationship of trait anger to resting blood pressure: a meta-analysis. Health Psychol. 1995 Sep;14(5):444-56. doi: 10.1037//0278-6133.14.5.444. PMID: 7498116.

4. Jorgensen RS, Johnson BT, Kolodziej ME, Schreer GE. Elevated blood pressure and personality: a meta-analytic review. Psychol Bull. 1996 Sep;120(2):293-320. doi: 10.1037/0033-2909.120.2.293. PMID: 8831299.

5. Rainforth MV, Schneider RH, Nidich SI, Gaylord-King C, Salerno JW, Anderson JW. Stress reduction programs in patients with elevated blood pressure: a systematic review and meta-analysis. Curr Hypertens Rep. 2007 Dec;9(6):520-8. doi: 10.1007/s11906-007-0094-3. PMID: 18350109; PMCID: PMC2268875.

6. Park SH, Han KS. Blood Pressure Response to Meditation and Yoga: A Systematic Review and Meta-Analysis. J Altern Complement Med. 2017 Sep;23(9):685-695. doi: 10.1089/acm.2016.0234. Epub 2017 Apr 6. PMID: 28384004.

7. Mann SJ. Job stress and blood pressure: A critical appraisal of reported studies. Curr. Hypertens. Rev. 2006;2(2):127-138. doi:10.2174/157340206776877389.

8. Fauvel JP, M'Pio I, Quelin P, Rigaud JP, Laville M, Ducher M. Neither perceived job stress nor individual cardiovascular reactivity predict high blood pressure. Hypertension. 2003 Dec;42(6):1112-6. doi: 10.1161/01. HYP.0000102862.93418.EE. Epub 2003 Nov 3. PMID: 14597647.

9. Marshall BJ, Warren JR. Unidentified curved bacilli in the stomach of patients with gastritis and peptic ulceration. Lancet. 1984 Jun 16;1(8390):1311-5. doi: 10.1016/s0140-6736(84)91816-6. PMID: 6145023.

10. Jones MP. The role of psychosocial factors in peptic ulcer disease: beyond Helicobacter pylori and NSAIDs. J Psychosom Res. 2006 Apr;60(4):407-12. doi: 10.1016/j.jpsychores.2005.08.009. PMID: 16581366.

11. Cohen H. Peptic ulcer and Helicobacter pylori. Gastroenterol Clin North Am. 2000 Dec;29(4):775-89. doi: 10.1016/s0889-8553(05)70146-1. PMID: 11190063.

12. Levenstein S. Psychosocial factors in peptic ulcer and inflammatory bowel disease. J Consult Clin Psychol. 2002 Jun;70(3):739-50. doi: 10.1037//0022-006x.70.3.739. PMID: 12090380.

Chapter 2

The Psychosocial
History

W*hen, as physicians, we see a patient,* the information
we obtain to determine a diagnosis derives from three
main sources: the history, the physical exam, and diagnostic tests.
It is said that 90 percent of the information needed to make a diagnosis comes from the history alone. I believe that. While writing
this book, I reflected on how my history-taking has evolved since
my days as a medical student, and how it continues to evolve.

My classmates and I began seeing patients in the third year of
medical school. We learned how to obtain the patient's history by
listening to his or her description of their illness, asking questions
about it, then asking a further series of questions as if from a script
to complete the medical history.

During residency, as we obtained medical histories from hun-
dreds of patients, we gradually learned to ask the essential questions
pretty efficiently. The psychosocial history consisted mostly of
asking whether the patient was single or married, had children,

the kind of work they did, whether they suffered from anxiety or depression, and whether they drank, smoked, or used drugs. The family history focused on the age and health of their parents and siblings. If any had died, we asked their age at the time of death, and the cause of death.

Although obtaining the medical history became a straightforward task, obtaining the psychosocial history is an art that evolves over many years. I regularly asked patients about stress, and whether they were suffering from anxiety or depression. Patients would bring up what was troubling them the most, sometimes very personal issues. I learned through experience how to discuss some of those issues with patients.

It is hard not to learn from years of intimate conversations with thousands of patients. This is not textbook learning, but an education I was immersed in, day after day, for decades. For a time, I met with a psychologist every few weeks to discuss the patients I was seeing, the issues that arose, what those issues meant, and how to respond. I also read articles and book chapters. But mostly, my learning was from my patients.

There were barriers to those conversations. Getting the necessary information, both medical and psychosocial, is essential to optimize and individualize patient care, but it can take time. And the practice of medicine has become increasingly pressured for time. Some patients communicate information efficiently. Others don't. And a psychosocial history sometimes seems like a time-consuming luxury. But I came to appreciate how often it is at the heart of medicine.

At first, I had neither the experience, the perspective, nor the gravitas to comfortably ask deeply personal questions, especially when talking with patients much older than I, as most were. But over years and decades, I began to ask more personal questions, not out of idle curiosity, but in an effort to obtain a good sense of the patient and how one's personal history might be affecting his or her health or general state of being. In answering my questions, some patients brought up events or personal issues they might not have discussed for decades, or ever told anyone; events that sometimes bore relevance to their treatment.

One limitation is that usually the only visit with enough built-in time to inquire carefully about the patient's psychosocial history is the first visit. Having just met the patient, I sometimes felt I was being overly intrusive, and sometimes asked the patient if he or she felt I was being intrusive. To this day I remain surprised at how rarely a patient said "yes." On the contrary, patients often welcomed my questions, feeling that I was making an effort to know them, and perhaps embracing the opportunity to discuss issues they had never spoken about with anyone.

I came to realize that many patients felt comfortable confiding sensitive issues in the context of the doctor/patient relationship. I also realized the impact confiding can have, an impact I witnessed repeatedly. More surprising, for some patients, the impact was immediate.

I came to see the effect of offering reassurance as an important, yet too often overlooked, intervention in the physician's armamentarium. I had always been comfortable offering patients reassurance regarding their medical issues, and, when appropriate, allaying their fears concerning their condition. But offering reassurance vis-a-vis emotional issues was a very different matter.

In my early years as a physician, I felt inexperienced and untrained in that realm. Over time, I came to realize the benefit reassurance could provide for patients dealing with adversity. I was surprised by how much my words—and the words of any physician—could mean. Additionally, I knew the reassurance had to be sincere; not just words.

In this era in which patients frequently move, or have their insurance coverage shifted or canceled, a patient is less able than in the past to maintain a relationship with the same physician for years and decades. It is a great loss. I feel comfortable when I can say to a patient whom I've known for years, at a time of crisis: "I know you. I know you'll be all right." I know the patient well enough to say it, and the patient has known me long enough to accept it and to know they are not just scripted words.

As I became more comfortable having intimate discussions with patients, I found myself further expanding the psychosocial history I was obtaining. I began to realize that there was more to it than just asking about current stress. The patient's life history, particularly his or her childhood experiences, often bore more relevance than a recitation of recent stresses.

I began to ask more patients about their childhood and how events from their past had affected them. Some had been impacted unendingly, and the roots of some of their current issues, both emotional and physical, lay in their past experiences.

Perhaps the most striking and surprising observation was the phenomenon of the patient who had been through hell and was fine, and could tell me that he or she had put the trauma behind them and moved on with no lingering effects. They were not saying they were avoiding those emotions. They were saying they were unaware of any emotion or impact related to those events. Without my questions, many had never even mentioned the roughest events of their life.

I was amazed at the resilience of many patients and wondered how they had moved on so successfully following what were often traumatic events. I also wondered whether those events, though patients had no awareness of any emotion related to them, could still be affecting them, emotionally, physically, or both. It stirred in me a consuming interest in this aspect of resilience and its role in the mind-body connection; looking at the patient's story rather than focusing only on the emotional distress he or she reported feeling. I was becoming increasingly aware of the critical protective effect of *not* feeling. At the same time, I was beginning to sense that emotions that were not felt, whether from day-to-day life or events and experiences that had occurred years or even decades earlier, might be contributory to current medical conditions whose cause remained inadequately explained. I recognized that patients, doctors, and researchers rarely if ever consider attributing medical consequences to emotions that patients don't feel, don't mention, and aren't aware of.

These observations were pointing me toward an understanding of the mind-body connection that differed from the long-standing focus on the role of current emotional distress.

+ + + + + + + + + + + +

As physicians we never stop learning, never stop tweaking—and never should stop tweaking—how we practice medicine. That's why we use the term "practice." Even after decades of practice, my interaction with patients continues to evolve.

In our first years in medical school, we are told that our best teachers will be our patients. This is absolutely true.

Chapter 3

Noticing the Missing Emotions
Hypertension as a Physiologic Telltale

M*y clinical experience treating patients* with hypertension was consistent with the studies I was reading; studies that failed to confirm that stress caused hypertension. However, I was also beginning to realize that in some patients it did, but, in them, the mind-body connection seemed to differ drastically from popular beliefs.

I was observing that hypertension was rarely a mind-body disorder in patients with relatively ordinary hypertension, (i.e., mild or moderate hypertension that can be brought under control with a change in health habits and/or with one or two of the standard medications). Their hypertension was attributable to either or both of two factors: genetic predisposition, as evident in family history, or lifestyle factors such as sodium intake, overweight, diet, and lack of exercise.

However, I found myself intrigued much more by the 5 to 10 percent or so of patients who had hypertension that clearly differed from the ordinary. They presented with one of four forms of hypertension (Table 1): paroxysmal (episodic) hypertension; severe or resistant hypertension; unexplained hypertension in young individuals (in their teens or twenties); and, in some, hypertension that began suddenly rather than gradually.

The atypical presentation of their hypertension begged for an explanation. In most such patients, we search for a cause such as underlying kidney disease, narrowing of an artery to a kidney, or excessive secretion by the adrenal gland of a hormone such as aldosterone or adrenaline. The ingestion of a medication—birth control pills, anti-inflammatory drugs, steroids, and others—can also cause blood pressure elevation. However, testing identifies a cause in only about 10 percent of such cases; in the others, the origin of these perplexing forms of hypertension remains a lifelong mystery.

It was among these patients in whom I noticed an unsuspected mind-body origin, one strikingly different from traditional beliefs. This understanding came from listening to the stories they told and asking questions that uncovered information that patients otherwise might not have communicated.

At first, I thought their stories were merely coincidental. But I was much more likely to hear those stories from patients with these unexplained forms of hypertension than from patients with more routine hypertension. I realized that their history was, in fact, a clue to the origin of their hypertensive disorder.

Table 1: Four Forms of Hypertension with an Unsuspected Mind-Body Connection:

Hypertension That Developed Suddenly (Ch. 4)	Paroxysmal (Episodic) Hypertension (Ch. 5)
Severe, Resistant Hypertension (Ch. 6)	Hypertension Beginning at a Young Age (Ch. 6)

In the following chapters I will describe what I noticed, and how it made the role of emotions hidden from our awareness obvious and, frankly, unavoidable. More important, I'll show how this understanding pertains to—and offers new treatment options for—patients with other medical conditions. Even if you don't have hypertension, I am confident you will find the upcoming chapters interesting, informative, and relevant.

Chapter 4

The First Lessons
Hypertension That Developed Suddenly

O*ften, the evidence we seek* is right under our noses, but we don't notice it. In this chapter I will present the brief yet revealing stories of two patients.

Jim, 44, was tall, slim, very successful, and recently married. A few months before he saw me, he'd been diagnosed with incurable metastatic cancer. He was referred to me after he suddenly developed severe hypertension.

Hypertension typically comes on gradually, with borderline or intermittent mild blood pressure elevation, and subsequently, over a period of months to years, more sustained elevation. Jim's hypertension had not followed this pattern. It began with sudden, severe elevation. He had lost 30 pounds due to a reduced appetite, which, if anything, should have lowered, not raised, his blood pressure.

Severe hypertension that develops suddenly is not ordinary hypertension. It begs for an explanation. Physicians usually order tests to find a cause, but the results of Jim's tests had been unrevealing.

It was conceivable, but unlikely, that his malignant tumor was secreting a hormone, undetected by blood tests, that was raising his blood pressure. However, no such hormone has been associated with this type of tumor.

Yet there had to be a cause.

There seemed to be an obvious, likely cause: severe emotional distress concerning his recent diagnosis of cancer and its poor prognosis. I'll never forget Jim's answer when I asked if he was very upset. He responded, seriously and not sarcastically: "No, I'm not upset. Why should I be upset? It's my wife who should be upset."

He truly did not feel upset! Yet his blood pressure had gone haywire.

Jim said he'd always been an optimist. He was always "up." Among his siblings, he was always the "breath of fresh air." This is exactly the way we would all want to be. Of course, now he was facing a crisis that seriously challenged one's ability to remain optimistic. He had virtually no chance to survive. And he knew it. Yet even in this circumstance, he did not feel upset.

Jim's case, even by itself, dramatically suggested an entirely different understanding of stress and hypertension. The emotionally challenging crisis he faced offered a conspicuous explanation for the sudden onset of severe hypertension at a time when he was eating little and losing weight. Had he been distraught, everyone would have attributed his hypertension to his state of mind. But here, brutal stress was raising Jim's blood pressure without any awareness by him of emotional distress.

Jim wasn't saying he was trying to divert his attention away from his awful situation, or that he was confident he would be fine. He was not in denial. He knew he was dying, yet, without trying to block out the emotions, he did not feel distraught. He seemed to have a lifelong trait of not feeling stressful emotion.

I thought perhaps it was fortunate that Jim was not feeling troubled. Otherwise, he might have been too emotionally overwhelmed to function during his little remaining time.

Jim's hypertension makes sense only if we consider his story, regardless of the absence of reported emotional distress. What stood out, the hidden clue to the mind-body connection, was the conspicuous absence, in a horrible situation, of the emotional pain that would have been expected.

Jim's otherwise unexplained blood pressure elevation, as well as subsequent similar stories from numerous other patients, told me that we can be affected by powerful emotions—even if we are unaware of those emotions.

Another patient with the sudden onset of severe hypertension whose story also provoked my awareness of the role of unfelt emotions was someone I never met. I received a phone call from a medical resident who sought my advice concerning a patient with uncontrolled severe hypertension. The doctor told me this story:

The patient, just 32 years old, had suddenly developed severe hypertension. His blood pressure had not responded to a standard combination of two medications that target renal (kidney) mechanisms of hypertension, and it was still extremely elevated at 180/120.

With the sudden onset of the hypertension, its severity, the young age of the patient, and the ineffectiveness of the two medications, this was clearly not an ordinary case of hypertension. There had to be an explanation. The resident said that the necessary tests had been performed and had not revealed a cause.

There had to be a reason. A 32-year-old man does not suddenly develop severe hypertension out of nowhere. Given the suddenness and severity of the blood pressure elevation and the absence of an identifiable medical cause, I wondered about stress; it would have to be severe stress because day-to-day stress does not do this.

Yes, the resident had considered that possibility, and yes, there was a source of severe stress: The patient had recently been diagnosed with AIDS. This was in the late 1980s, when there was no treatment for AIDS. The diagnosis was a virtual death sentence. But the resident said he did not think the hypertension was related to that horrible news because the patient was not upset about it. "He seemed really 'cool' with it."

Here again, the abrupt onset of serious, otherwise unexplained hypertension that coincided with obviously enormous stress could not have been a coincidence. This story reinforced my reaction to Jim's story. It told me the mind-body connection can be operative even when, and perhaps especially when, a patient is unaware of emotional distress.

In nearly all patients with "essential hypertension," the hypertension is mediated either by the kidneys, or by the sympathetic nervous system (SNS), or by both. In 80 percent or more of patients, it is driven by the kidneys. This form of hypertension can be called "nephrogenic" hypertension, and responds well to medications that target the kidneys, including diuretics, angiotensin-converting enzyme inhibitors (ACE inhibitors), angiotensin receptor blockers (ARBs), and the vasodilating calcium channel blockers. In others, it is driven by the SNS and is called "neurogenic" hypertension. And in some it is driven by both the kidneys and the SNS.

Normally, our SNS tone increases and decreases with emotion, with our blood pressure rising and falling accordingly throughout the day. This is normal physiology; it is not hypertension. Since the emotions we feel stimulate the SNS and transiently raise our blood pressure, one would think that sustained hypertension driven by the SNS could also be linked to the emotion we feel. Yet in looking at patients, such a link does not seem apparent, leaving the etiology of the increased SNS tone a mystery.

Hypertension driven by the SNS responds best to medications that target the SNS; for example, a beta-receptor blocker, alone or in combination with an alpha-receptor blocker. Drugs like clonidine are also effective, but I try not to prescribe them because of side effects such as fatigue that are associated with their use.

In this patient, the non-response to a combination of two medications that target the kidneys suggested that his severe hypertension was driven by the SNS rather than by the kidneys. Involvement of the SNS was also suggested by the severe stress the patient was encountering, even in the absence of apparent emotional distress.

I suggested replacing his medication with a combination of a beta-blocker and an alpha-blocker. The patient's blood pressure promptly normalized, further implicating an SNS origin, though the patient had insisted he did not feel distressed.

In both cases the key finding was evident by looking at what was conspicuously missing. The absence of emotion generally does not provoke attention, but here it was hard for me not to notice. The unusual stories of these and other patients forced me to consider a mind-body connection that differed sharply from traditional views and pointed to new treatment approaches.

Chapter 5

Solving the Long-standing Mystery of Paroxysmal Hypertension

The importance of offering a new understanding of the mind-body connection lies in whether it can help us understand the origin of various medical conditions, and, more important, whether it can lead to improvement in treatment. The patients from whom I learned the most were those with a dramatic and often disabling form of hypertension that had remained unexplained and ineffectively treated: severe paroxysmal (episodic) hypertension.

The new understanding of the mind-body connection I gained from seeing patients with this dramatic form of hypertension is obvious in their stories, and in the success of treatment based on this understanding. And it was the blatant example provided by patients with this disorder that opened the door to consideration of a similar unnoticed mind-body connection relevant to many other medical conditions.

In this chapter I present my experience with patients with this disorder and the lessons it teaches that pertain to numerous other medical disorders. To date, this understanding remains the only explanation for paroxysmal hypertension. More important, treatment based on this understanding remains the only effective treatment, and fortunately is effective in almost all patients.

Patients with paroxysmal (episodic) hypertension experience sudden unprovoked episodes of severe and symptomatic blood pressure elevation, often with an increase in heart rate. These episodes often result in ER visits and hospitalizations. The attacks occur "out of the blue," and patients insist they are not related to stress or anxiety.

Every physician, and I mean *every* physician, immediately suspects that an adrenaline–producing tumor of the adrenal gland, called a pheochromocytoma, or, for short, a "pheo," is the cause of these sudden bursts of severe blood pressure elevation, and orders tests to determine if that tumor is present. But only 1 percent of patients turn out to have a pheo.[1] In the other 99 percent, the cause and treatment had remained a complete, long-standing mystery.

Joseph was among the first patients I saw with this disorder. His blood pressure had been normal until he began experiencing episodes of sudden and severe blood pressure elevation. He would suddenly experience a severe headache and flushing and feel so unwell that he feared he was at risk of a stroke . . . or death. His blood pressure would increase to 230/120, an extremely high level, especially in someone who had never had hypertension.

These episodes had been occurring for over two years, about once every week or two. They would last a few hours and then his blood pressure level would subside; the attacks left him exhausted for the rest of the day.

Joseph had been hospitalized twice and had been to emergency rooms about eight times. Every doctor he encountered immediately suspected a pheo, but test results made it clear he did not have a pheo. The cause remained unknown, and he continued to experience these frightening episodes. Treatment with antihypertensive drugs failed to prevent or alter those attacks.

I asked Joseph if the attacks were related to stress. He insisted, as do nearly all patients with this disorder, that they were not, and occurred "out of the blue." He said he had little stress in his life and that the attacks could not have a mind-body origin.

Joseph was a Holocaust survivor. Decades earlier, he had lost his family and had spent two years in a concentration camp. With no other explanation for his condition, I wondered if the erratic and sudden changes in blood pressure typically driven by the SNS could stem from lingering effects of the trauma he had endured decades earlier.

He disagreed, stating that he had put that experience behind him and that it had had no lingering emotional impact. He had never suffered from anxiety or depression and had never felt the need to see a psychotherapist.

Listening to Joseph provided an "aha" moment: I was seeing someone who was a survivor of horrific trauma who felt no residual emotion whatsoever, yet was suffering from a disorder mediated by the SNS, whose main trigger is emotion.

Barbara, 53, had suffered from paroxysmal hypertension for a few years. Like Joseph, she had been to the emergency room several times. As with Joseph, antihypertensive drugs prescribed by her doctors had been ineffective in preventing or mitigating recurrent attacks.

Life was good, and here, too, this did not seem to be a stress-related disorder. But my experience with patients with this disorder led me to ask further questions.

When Barbara was 29, her husband died in a car accident. She had had to deal with the simultaneous tasks of grieving the death of her life partner, comforting and raising her two children, and struggling to survive financially. Now, decades later, at a much better time in life, she was suffering unexplained episodes of severe hypertension.

I broached the possibility of a connection between that tragic period and the current medical problem. Like Joseph, and like most patients I see with this disorder, Barbara was skeptical that an event from decades earlier that was not currently troubling her could be related to her hypertensive attacks.

I asked how she'd gotten through those first years. Did she grieve? Her answer was one that other patients with this disorder have also given, almost verbatim: "Who had time to grieve?"

Barbara had faced a grave crisis, one which had put her at high risk of being overwhelmed and unable to function. Her emotional survival depended on her *not* feeling the depth of emotional pain at hand. She had never grieved the sudden, tragic loss of her young husband. She'd survived, and had survived well, with those emotions kept, as if by autopilot, out of her awareness.

Frank, 65, was a corporate CEO until he was disabled by hypertensive episodes. The attacks came out of nowhere, "out of the blue," about once a week. Between episodes, his blood pressure was normal. Tests for a pheo were negative.

Frank was a do-er, not a feeler. He had never been anxious or depressed. Nothing fazed him. Throughout his life he had what has been called a "repressive coping style."

Over the past four decades I have seen over two hundred patients who suffered from paroxysmal hypertension. Most reported a past history of overwhelming stress or trauma. Others, even without a history of conspicuous trauma, seemed impervious to the effects of day-to-day stress.

Many had had multiple ER visits and hospital stays and had gone from doctor to doctor without identification of a cause or effective treatment. Between episodes, their blood pressure was much lower, and, in many, it was normal. In many, the continuing risk of an attack at any time had interfered with their jobs and their ability to make plans. Worse, the episodes continued to recur for years. They were an ongoing problem.

Transient elevation of blood pressure at moments of emotional stress is a normal physiologic reaction. It is driven by stimulation of the SNS, which increases the secretion of adrenaline and noradrenaline. The increased levels of adrenaline and/or noradrenaline in blood samples I obtained from patients during an attack were consistent with my assumption that the SNS was involved.[2]

Strikingly, almost every patient insisted the attacks were unprovoked and unrelated to current emotional distress. Ironically, in most, the first attack occurred at a time when life was the best it had ever been. So although it is well known that emotional distress stimulates the SNS, a mind-body origin had never been considered a possibility.

My understanding of the origin of paroxysmal hypertension began with the observation that most patients reported a period in their past, even from as far back as childhood, of overwhelming stress or significant trauma.[3] And, again, what also stood out was the insistence by most that those events had had no emotional consequences. They did not report ongoing problems such as anxiety, depression, or PTSD. They did not use the phrase: "You never completely get over it," a term I hear frequently from patients without this disorder who have lost a loved one.

Remarkably, they seemed the most resilient of trauma survivors. Most had moved on in their lives without significant psychological impairment. The absence of awareness of emotional pain seemed to be at the heart of their resilience. At the same time, it also seemed to be characteristic of, and, I suspected, an unrecognized cause of, their paroxysmal hypertension. Their conspicuous non-reaction had never been noticed.

My patients were teaching me that not feeling devastating emotions was at the core of their emotional resilience. But I increasingly suspected that those emotions, though unfelt, must persist beneath conscious awareness; there was no other explanation for these unexplained bursts of SNS activity years—or decades—later.

Some patients, like Frank, manifested a pattern of not feeling emotional distress regardless of life circumstances. They were super even-keeled. If I asked if they'd ever suffered from anxiety or depression, their response was "never," regardless of the stress they had faced in life. They were a rock on whom others depended; a rock who needed no one's emotional support.

The Ultimate Proof
Is Treatment Based on This Understanding Effective?

Hearing the stories of patient after patient convinced me that paroxysmal hypertension was linked to unfelt emotions. The term most aligned to the phenomenon I was seeing was the repression of emotions, where the emotions are kept from awareness without conscious effort, and without awareness that they linger within.

I knew that the best proof of this understanding, and its value, lay in whether it could lead to effective treatment. I saw two possible approaches: a) healing through gaining conscious awareness of emotions that had been repressed, or the seemingly opposite approach: b) treatment with a medication that could fortify the barrier keeping emotions out of conscious awareness.

Healing Through Gaining Awareness

I wondered if gaining conscious awareness of long-repressed emotions could have a healing effect, but I knew there were barriers. Those emotions had been repressed for good reason, and the barriers had to be strong ones. Even tougher, these patients were not suffering from emotional discomfort; they had had no reason to see a psychologist to explore emotions they were unaware of. Many could not see the possibility of their disorder being related to emotions, let alone emotions from the distant past. Even if they were open to this understanding, did they want to explore those emotions?

I also had to consider that repressed emotions related to severe trauma might best be left alone. These patients had not come to me seeking to get in touch with those emotions. Also, could there be a danger in pulling down the barrier protecting against awareness? Could those emotions be overwhelming, even now? Could healing awareness be an option for some but not others?

There has been almost no research into this question in patients with a medical condition who, in the absence of emotional distress, are not seen by psychologists. They differ from post-traumatic patients who see a psychologist specifically because of emotional symptoms.

The Alternative of an Antidepressant

I thought about the alternative of prescribing a medication such as an antidepressant, wondering if it could strengthen the barrier that was keeping those emotions out of awareness, and in doing so eliminate the attacks. Since blood pressure medications have never been found to be effective in preventing paroxysms, and since many of the patients had been suffering for years without any effective treatment, why not try it?

I could not imagine suggesting that Joseph seek awareness of Holocaust-related emotions that seemed to have been repressed for decades. I recommended trying an antidepressant. He did not like the idea. He felt no emotional distress and saw no reason to take an antidepressant. He seemed offended by the suggestion and did not return for three months. When he did, although he doubted it would work, he had no other alternative.

The attacks stopped two weeks after starting the medication. He remained on the medication for years and suffered no further attacks.

Barbara also responded to an antidepressant; her attacks ceased.

Frank, like Joseph, did not like my idea of trying an antidepressant. But he was a pragmatist. I reminded him that there was no known effective treatment and he had nothing to lose if he tried an antidepressant. If it did not work or if he experienced side effects, he could always stop it.

Frank sneered. But in the absence of an alternative, he took the prescription. He had no further attacks.

I still wondered: could repressed emotions be brought to awareness? If so, could that alleviate or even "cure" the disorder? I was discouraged because in the absence of emotional distress most patients had no interest in exploring this possible understanding with a psychotherapist. Yes, they were experiencing distress surrounding their current medical situation, but not about the events underlying it.

Then, I met Cindy.

Cindy, 56, had been suffering from episodes of paroxysmal hypertension every few weeks for five years. Tests for a pheo were negative. There was no explanation, and treatment had been ineffective.

Cindy, previously divorced, was happily remarried. She had two grown children. She was not suffering from major stress or emotional distress. She smiled frequently and easily.

I inquired further about her life history.

Cindy came from a typical White middle-class home in Connecticut, with "good enough" parents. There had been no abuse or trauma.

She had grown up in the 1960s, the "flower child" era. She had been a hippie, involved with anti-war protests, drugs, and everything else. She married her boyfriend and quickly had two children.

As she approached her thirties, the freedom of being a flower child had been replaced by the sobering responsibilities of raising two children. She had evolved from her wild teens. Her husband had not. He drank every day, always had a supply of marijuana, and had not "grown up."

Cindy faced a difficult decision. She felt she could no longer plan a future around her husband but was terrified about the consequences of leaving him. She finally decided she needed to leave him and move on.

The years afterward were incredibly hard. She finished college while holding two jobs and raising two small children. This was not a brief stressful period; she endured that life for several years.

Her children grew up and were fine. Cindy ultimately remarried (not to a flower child). Her life was in the best shape it had been in decades. That is when she began to experience *the hypertensive attacks. If current stress were the cause, this was the least likely time for her to be stricken with it.*

Listening to Cindy's story, I could readily see that she had managed to get through a long period of enormous stress that could have overwhelmed anyone. I asked further:

"How did you manage to get through those years?"

"You do what you have to do."

"Did you cry much, or get depressed?"

"No, never."

I was struck again by her use of that word, "never."

I discussed my reactions with Cindy. I explained how most patients with her type of hypertension described a history of trauma or severe life challenges that they had handled incredibly well, without having fallen apart emotionally. Cindy listened.

I saw her three weeks later. She said that during those three weeks she had cried every day about those years.

Her hypertensive attacks ceased, without medication. She did not require psychotherapy. Fifteen years later, she is still doing well.

Cindy had brought into awareness emotions that had been repressed for decades. It never occurred to her that she had repressed them. I believe she was now better able to tolerate those emotions, knowing she had survived the years-long crisis and that her life was now stable. Had her life still been a mess, I believe the barrier to awareness would have been more necessary and more insurmountable.

The sudden end to her paroxysms after five years, with no intervention except the emotional experience of those few weeks, by itself, provided unassailable proof that paroxysmal hypertension is, indeed, a mind-body disorder. It also demonstrated that overpowering emotions hidden from awareness can and do persist within us for decades, and can eventually lead to problems such as a hypertensive disorder. Her story provided strong empirical evidence that gaining awareness of emotions repressed long ago is possible, and, in the absence of other treatments, could end five years of hypertensive attacks.

There was another important lesson from Cindy's story. Although repressing painful emotions could now be seen as the cause of her disorder, the repression was also a key component of her resilience, a gift that had enabled her to function well and get through those extremely difficult years.

Cindy's story also raised the question of whether repression of emotions might also be at the root of other inadequately explained medical disorders, and whether gaining awareness could be effective in treating those disorders as well. These were questions rarely asked in the annals of medicine.

One aspect of Cindy's story was problematic: In studies concerning trauma, her history would not be regarded as trauma. Divorce is unfortunately common, and there was no issue of "abuse." Trauma questionnaires used in studies would not identify the difficult years that followed Cindy's divorce as "trauma." Overwhelming stress, yes, but not trauma. Further, she had survived without developing any diagnosable psychological problem and had never needed to see a psychologist.

Trauma questionnaires do not identify a mind-body link in patients like Cindy, even though a mind-body origin was clear. In this respect, a questionnaire cannot replace a careful clinical interview.

+ + + + + + + + + + + +

Finally, I also wondered: When is gaining awareness an option, and when isn't it? The stories of these two patients suggest at least a partial answer.

James
The Best of the Best

America is a country of immigrants. We encounter immigrants every day, but don't know what it is like to be an immigrant, as most of us were born here after someone from a previous generation made the decision to leave their homeland and come here.

James, 71, had felt well his entire life. He was thin, did not smoke, watched his diet, exercised, and looked young for his age. He had never been hospitalized and had had no medical problems. Except one.

Five years earlier he had begun to experience sudden bouts of severe blood pressure elevation, to levels as high as 230/120. He would feel pain and a pounding in his head and then feel himself trembling. The episodes would last up to a few hours. He was terrified that he would suffer a stroke during an episode. At first, the episodes occurred about twice a year, but in the past few months they had been occurring about twice a week. He was afraid to make plans to go anywhere.

He had seen several doctors. All suspected he had a pheo, but repeated testing had been negative. They had no answer. When he continued to ask why he was having these attacks, one even replied to him that he was crazy.

James was married, had two grown children, was financially secure, and had little stress. He seemed humble, yet proud of his achievements. Nothing overt suggested a mind-body connection.

I asked about past trauma. James said there had been none. He'd grown up in a close family, came here, succeeded, and was close to his children, who were doing well.

I inquired further about his life story.

He was a native of South Korea.

"How old were you when you arrived in the U.S.?"

"Twenty."

"With anyone or by yourself?"

"By myself."

"What made you decide to come here?"

"We all saw America as the greatest place in the world." *His face lit up. "We all dreamed of living in America."*

"How did you manage when you got here? Did you know anyone?"

"No. I came on a student visa, so to stay I made sure to enroll at a local college."

He worked his way through college, then set up a grocery business he was still operating.

I inquired further.

Over decades James had supported his children and put them through college while using any money he'd saved to bring other family members here, one by one, from South Korea. He was the rock of the family. He worked from 7:00 a.m. to 11:00 p.m., seven days a week. His daughter, who was with him in my office, said he didn't take a vacation until she was nineteen.

He helped relatives who came to him when they needed financial assistance. And he won an award as "Immigrant of the Year" for all he had done for immigrants within the community.

James's story was a classic immigrant success story.

I asked him: "You took care of so many people. Who took care of you?"

I knew what his answer was going to be.

"I took care of myself."

James had had a tough life. He did for everyone while demanding nothing from anyone. He handled everything. And he'd never been overwhelmed; had never suffered from anxiety or depression.

I paused for a few moments, sitting quietly.

"I hear your story. I can imagine how hard it must have been."

He sat silently. Staring straight ahead, he responded with great difficulty.

"It . . . was . . . so . . . tough."

His eyes began to well up.

James, like Cindy, had a story to tell from decades earlier. He similarly insisted that the past had not affected him emotionally. He had not suffered a traumatic event. A formal trauma questionnaire would not have identified any trauma. But his story revealed that without question he had endured, with a will of steel and likely with the help of repression, decades of struggling. His story could easily have been overlooked.

My first intervention was to offer James the desperately needed reassurance that I offer patients with this disorder—that based on my experience it was unlikely that he would suffer a stroke or die during an episode. He had been terrified about that. Further proof: he had not suffered a stroke despite five years of attacks.

I also offered him the reassurance the other doctors he'd seen had not: "No, you're not crazy. On the contrary, you endured those very rough years amazingly well."

James had been a rock of strength in his family. I was sincere about his emotional strength, and I'm confident he got that.

I prescribed an anti-anxiety pill, alprazolam (Xanax), that he could take, if needed, at the onset of an attack. And I was considering prescribing an antidepressant to prevent future attacks. I offered him the reassurance that I was confident that the disorder was treatable and he would be fine.

In parting I asked if he had ever discussed the stress of those years with his family. No, never. I urged him to talk with his family, and, for the first time, share that which he had held alone all those decades.

James returned to see me a few times in the ensuing months. He said he'd been discussing those years with his family. Over a few weeks, the attacks diminished in severity and frequency, then ceased, without any medication. The unexplained

years-long medical ordeal was over, after unearthing that which
for decades he had never felt nor acknowledged.

No, James, you weren't and aren't crazy. On the contrary: You are among the best of the best.

Yes, it's exciting to begin a new life in America. It must also be terrifying. The lack of language, money, and family; the hard work, and the mystery of what might lie ahead. To succeed, or have the courage to do it, I again look at the gift of repression. Jim's story and Cindy's, and, over the years, the stories of so many other patients told me that repression is not psychopathology. It is a gift, a blessing of the human mind that, when operative, enables us to keep potentially overwhelming emotional distress out of our awareness, and prevents us from being overcome by fear or despair.

James and Cindy's stories also show the limitations of formal trauma questionnaires. The questionnaires identify forms of trauma, but they overlook a history such as theirs of prolonged and severe emotional stress. Even in the absence of "trauma," being able to function and survive emotionally in the face of prolonged emotional stress for which there is no clear end in sight, often requires repression of the cumulative emotional distress. Again, careful clinical inquiry picks up what rigid questionnaires do not.

Cindy and James responded dramatically to uncovering previously repressed emotions. The healing they experienced confirmed my growing belief that repressed emotions related to a history of massive emotional stress or trauma can lie unsuspected at the heart of this disorder. These patients were also teaching me that their repression, although the cause of their hypertensive disorder, was also at the heart of their resilience.

I still wondered: Was there a way to tell who among the patients with this disorder might be able to heal in this manner and who might not? Ling's story suggested a demarcation.

Ling had been on medication for difficult-to-control hypertension for decades. But in the six months prior to her first visit, she had begun experiencing episodes of sudden and severe blood pressure elevation to over 230/130 mmHg, accompanied by a fierce headache. There was no apparent trigger for the attacks. No major stress of any kind.

Previous testing had ruled out a pheo. By this point, my experience was telling me there was likely to be an underlying story. I asked her about her life, present and past.

Ling was happily married. Her husband, John, who was in the office with us, had been her classmate in medical school in China. He struck me as a wonderful, caring husband. They lived in Maryland and had two grown children who were well. She had retired after a long career as a physician.

I inquired about her past. She was 40 when she emigrated to the U.S. John had come first, and she followed. Not an unusual story.

Given her paroxysmal hypertension and its severity, I delved further.

When she and John were living in China, seeking to come to the U.S., Chinese government policy greatly discouraged that.

John finally received permission, and came here for further training, but was not allowed to bring his family with him. Ling and their two young children could not visit him, and he could not return to China to visit them without giving up his dream of staying in America.

Ling waited, not knowing when or if she would be allowed to join him. There was no telephone contact. Just a bi-monthly letter.

Four years later she was finally given the choice of joining him, with one condition: she could not bring their children, then 11 and 13. It might have been her only opportunity. She made the very difficult decision to join her husband. She parted from her children, who stayed with relatives. She didn't know how long she would be separated from them.

Two years later, the children were allowed to reunite with their parents.

By any definition, that had been a deeply painful time. Yet Ling was never depressed. She was sweet, but tough. She agreed that those were difficult times, but she thought it irrelevant because it had happened decades earlier and because she did not remain upset about it.

We talked about treatment options, of which I felt there were three. One was to get in touch with painful locked-up emotions and heal. However, Ling, feeling no emotion, saw no connection between those events and her current medical problem. A second option, best suited for patients with mild and infrequent episodes, was to take medication such as alprazolam (Xanax), an anxiolytic drug, or clonidine, a blood pressure drug, or a combination of the two, at the first sign of an episode. However, Ling's episodes were severe and *frequent. The third option was to prevent attacks with an antidepressant. My experience told me this could enable her to resume a normal life.*

Ling preferred the option of taking medication as needed. She disliked the idea of taking an antidepressant. After all, she wasn't depressed or anxious.

She returned a month or two later. She was worse. The attacks were occurring almost daily. And, hesitantly, she said there was something she hadn't told me: When she was 12, the youngest of five children, with no warning, her mother handed her over to an adoptive mother. I assumed it was for financial reasons. Ling moved away with her adoptive mother, a woman she described as cold. After that day, she rarely saw her family. In essence, in a single day she had cruelly lost both of her parents and all four of her siblings—her entire family.

Ling's story was among the most traumatic I have ever heard from a patient. I don't know if there was any other way a 12-year-old could have survived emotionally and moved on in life without repressing the intolerable pain of that event. She had survived, and ultimately had a remarkably normal and good life as an adult. She had never felt the need to see a psychologist. But the emotional scars, though fortunately unfelt, were there, and her hypertensive attacks seemed to indicate a weakening, with time or age, of that steel wall of repression. Ironically, and probably not coincidentally, her hypertensive attacks had begun shortly after a visit to China when, for the first time, she spent extended time with her adult siblings.

Hearing this part of Ling's story, I wondered if experiencing of emotions from the massive trauma she had endured at 12 would be too overwhelming, even now. And even if she were willing to see a psychologist, I thought it unlikely that months of "talk therapy" could break down the decades-old steel barrier of repression to which she owed her survival.

Given the severity and frequency of her attacks, and the severity of the trauma, I insisted that she start taking the antidepressant. This time she did not object. Ten days later, the hypertensive attacks ceased.

The cause of Ling's attacks, and the decision as to how to treat her condition, could be understood only by looking at her past, and at the emotions held within, emotions that were unfelt by virtue of the repression that had embraced and protected her, and had enabled her to move on with her life.

Her story also conveys another difficulty in unearthing the role of repressed emotions: patients often do not mention significant trauma—because it isn't on their minds or because deep down, they hesitate to go anywhere near it.

I suspected that experiencing those emotions and healing was probably not an option for Ling both because the trauma was so profound and because the repression, which had protected her from potentially terrible emotional consequences, was so powerful. I felt it wise to honor that repression, to leave it alone, and to reinforce that barrier with the help of an antidepressant.

+ + + + + + + + + + + +

Some patients with paroxysmal hypertension or other forms of hypertension (Chapter 6), or with other medical disorders (Chapters 11-14), experience a healing awareness, as Cindy and James did. Many, however, don't. My experience suggests that many survivors of severe trauma who are not consciously experiencing emotion related to the trauma are unlikely to penetrate that powerful and protective barrier of repression. Also, studies have not looked at the effect of psychological interventions such as psychotherapy in the management of survivors of severe trauma who coped successfully by virtue of repression and now present with medical conditions rather than with emotional distress. They haven't because the mind-body link is not suspected, and because patients do not seek counseling.

I believe we must consider the possibility that in the face of trauma or overwhelming stress, repression constituted the best possible defense in our emotional arsenal, and, in some, particularly survivors of severe trauma, it might be best to not challenge it. In this context I convey this understanding to patients, but I don't coerce unwilling or uninterested patients to attack that repression or to seek psychotherapy.

To summarize, in treating patients with paroxysmal hypertension, I don't recommend an antidepressant for every patient. In patients who experience mild, brief, and infrequent episodes, I offer reassurance that they are unlikely to suffer a catastrophic event such as a stroke during an episode, and I offer medication to take at the first sign of an attack, to shorten the attack. I recommend either clonidine, an anti-hypertensive drug that targets the sympathetic nervous system, or a rapid-acting anxiolytic drug, such as alprazolam (Xanax), or a combination of the two. In most patients, the attacks subside within 30 to 90 minutes. Many patients with mild, infrequent attacks find that treatment sufficient.

Some patients do experience a healing awareness of emotions that had been repressed for years or decades, and then do not require medication. This path to healing is less available, however, in survivors of severe trauma.

In patients with more severe or frequent attacks, particularly if they are interfering with their ability to function normally, it is clear that medication that could prevent attacks is needed. It is also clear that antihypertensive medications *do not prevent attacks.*

For those patients I offer the option of an antidepressant—not because they are depressed or anxious, but because it works in nearly all patients, by fortifying the barrier against awareness. I tell patients that even if my understanding of the disorder is incorrect, the response to the antidepressant is indisputable. I leave it to them to decide.

The success of treatment of paroxysmal hypertension based on this understanding has provided dramatic, repeated proof, that paroxysmal hypertension is a mind-body disorder that occurs despite the striking absence of perceived emotional distress, strongly implicating the role of repressed emotions. It also provides proof that repressed emotions can persist within us for decades. I published my findings about the origin and treatment of paroxysmal hypertension, including the success of treatment with antidepressants, over two decades ago.[3] Subsequently, another paper reported that treatment with the antidepressant sertraline was effective in preventing attacks in 90 percent of patients.[4]

In the two decades since my first report, no other explanation and no other treatment alternatives have been found, anywhere, for this disorder. Yet the concept of repressed emotions is so outside the range of thinking in medicine that I continue to see patient after patient who unnecessarily suffered for years without effective treatment.

Resistance to the concept of repressed emotions is considerable. I published my findings in an article in the Archives of Internal Medicine conveying the link between repressed emotions and paroxysmal hypertension, and the effectiveness of treatment with an antidepressant.[3] The manuscript was initially rejected. I wrote to the editor, arguing that the report needed to be published given the absence of any other explanation or treatment for the disorder and the prolonged suffering of patients. The editor then published the paper.

My recent review article on the topic of paroxysmal hypertension included a larger case series that further documented the prevention of recurrent paroxysms in 80–90 percent of patients treated with an antidepressant.[5] This intervention, which unfortunately physicians frequently fail to consider, remains the only one shown to be effective in preventing recurrent episodes.

References

1. Pacak K, Linehan WM, Eisenhofer G, Walther MM, Goldstein DS. Recent advances in genetics, diagnosis, localization, and treatment of pheochromocytoma. Ann Intern Med. 2001 Feb 20;134(4):315-29. doi: 10.7326/0003-4819-134-4-200102200-00016. PMID: 11182843.

2. Mann SJ. Severe paroxysmal hypertension. An autonomic syndrome and its relationship to repressed emotions. Psychosomatics. 1996 Sep-Oct;37(5):444-50. doi: 10.1016/S0033-3182(96)71532-3. PMID: 8824124.

3. Mann SJ. Severe paroxysmal hypertension (pseudopheochromocytoma): understanding the cause and treatment. Arch Intern Med. 1999 Apr 12;159(7):670-4. doi: 10.1001/archinte.159.7.670. PMID: 10218745.

4. Vaclavik J, Krenkova A, Kocianova E, Vaclavik T, Kamasova, M, Taborsky M (2015) Effect of sertraline in paroxysmal hypertension. J Hypertens 33(Suppl 1):e93. https://doi.org/10.1097/01.hjh.0000467601.49032.62

5. Mann SJ, Solanki KV. The cause and treatment of paroxysmal hypertension. Current Hypertension Reports 2022 (in press).

Chapter 6

Repressed Emotions in Other Forms of Hypertension

As *discussed above*, I believe that relatively routine cases of hypertension are not linked to a mind-body connection. Moving on from the observations in patients with paroxysmal hypertension, are there patients with other forms of hypertension in whom a burden of repressed emotions plays a role?

In this final chapter on hypertension, I will discuss the relationship between repressed emotions and two forms of hypertension that beg for an explanation: severe, resistant hypertension, and unexplained hypertension in young patients.

Severe, resistant hypertension

Most patients with hypertension have mild to moderate blood pressure elevation that can be well controlled with one, two, or perhaps three medications. The hypertension is usually attributable to genetics (family history) and health habits including weight, diet, sodium intake, and lack of exercise. It is not a mind-body disorder.

Where I came to suspect a mind-body connection linked to repressed emotions was among patients with severe and/or difficult-to-control hypertension who are at much higher risk of cardiovascular complications such as stroke, heart attack, and kidney disease. In most such patients, we don't know why they have such severe hypertension, or why their hypertension is resistant to treatment with multiple medications.

The proportion of treated patients considered to have "resistant" hypertension is about 14 percent.[1] And about 1 to 3 percent of patients have what is considered "refractory" hypertension, defined as hypertension that is not controlled despite taking five or more medications.[2,3] Patients with severe or refractory hypertension always trigger the question: Why? What is the cause? Physicians order tests seeking a cause, but despite decades of research, the cause remains an unsolved lifelong mystery in most.

Al, 35, had severe, truly uncontrollable hypertension. His blood pressure was usually above 170/120. He'd been having daily headaches for over six months. Treatment with a variety of medications had been ineffective.

Al's hypertension was unusual. It had started at a young age, was severe, and had not responded to medication. Testing for a cause had been unrevealing.

Al was not a "Type A," anxious, angry person. He appeared easygoing. I was surprised, though, when he described his current life situation. Because of the headaches, he'd had to stop working. He was living on dwindling savings. His wife was threatening to leave him (and eventually did).

I asked Al, given this stress, how his spirits were holding up. He responded genuinely, not sarcastically, that he was "as happy as a clam."

He remained on five medications. His blood pressure remained uncontrolled.

Given the enormity of stress in Al's life, it would have been perfectly understandable if he had acknowledged being severely anxious or depressed. And psychosomatic researchers would have readily attributed his hypertension to emotional stress.

Al's life was falling apart, yet he acknowledged none of the expected emotional distress. Perhaps he was being sarcastic, but not once in our several meetings did he communicate a hint of emotional upset, despite the enormity of his problems. This reaction was suggestive of a "repressive coping style." It was his calmness amid unrelenting stress. Along with it, he had unexplained and uncontrollable hypertension.

Few studies have considered or examined the possible link between severe, resistant hypertension and a history of trauma or a repressive coping style. Patients don't routinely mention trauma that occurred decades earlier. They are also unlikely to mention emotional distress if they have coped by means of repression. In the absence of overt psychological manifestations including anxiety, depression, PTSD, and others, physicians don't consider or ask about past trauma.

In my experience, many patients with severe refractory hypertension have a history of overwhelming stress or trauma that was dealt with through repression or what appears to be a repressive coping style. Their story is easy to miss as many do not report emotional angst.

Little has been published about a link between repressed emotions and severe hypertension. However, studies concerning response patterns to blood pressure medications do offer interesting insight. We found that the blood pressure of patients who reported a history of trauma, as assessed by the Childhood Trauma Questionnaire, were less likely than patients without a history of trauma to respond to medications that target the usual kidney-related (nephrogenic) causes of hypertension, suggesting that a mechanism other than the kidneys, (i.e., the sympathetic nervous system [SNS]), was operative.[4] And studies show that patients with refractory hypertension have increased SNS tone, again suggesting the role of emotion, even in the absence of overt emotional distress.[6] Studies also report that a repressive coping style is more common among patients with severe hypertension than among those with normal blood pressure or mild hypertension.[5]

The most severe form of unexplained hypertension is called "malignant essential hypertension." If untreated, in most patients it results in stroke, kidney failure, and/or death before the age of 50. It occurs disproportionately in patients of color. With the medications now available, we can control blood pressure in only some; in others, blood pressure is never adequately controlled.

Remarkably, research has failed to find a hormone, gene, or another biological explanation for most patients with this most severe form of hypertension. The usual mind-body focus on current emotional stress and distress has provided no insight. The role of repressed emotions has not been considered.

The first interesting clue I noticed before I had any awareness of the concept of repression was the fascinating coincidence that the patients I encountered with malignant essential hypertension tended to be extremely nice, calm people even though many described having had a very rough childhood. They were not angry or depressed, didn't have substance abuse problems, and were almost uniformly very pleasant individuals despite their rough childhood.

I had no statistics to quantify this, and there likely were exceptions, but when giving lectures I would sometimes ask the physicians in the audience if they had seen patients with malignant essential hypertension and whether they also experienced them as uncommonly calm, nice people. The answer was always: "Yes."

At the time, I didn't realize that, ironically, these patients' contentment despite their rough life history was a surprising clue that offered an explanation. Had they been angry, anxious, or depressed, their malignant hypertension would have readily been attributed to their emotional stress. Their equanimity despite all they had been through was contrary to what could have been expected but had never been noticed.

Frank, 33, a thin Black man, had perhaps the most severe, hard-to-control hypertension I've ever encountered. Extensive testing failed to uncover a cause. He grew up in Harlem, was married, and had a successful career. There was no particular stress in his life; he appeared very calm.

His family history revealed that his father had died at a young age. I, of course, wondered if the father's death might have been caused by severe hypertension. It hadn't. His father was hit by a car and died instantly. Frank was eleven. His father had been his best friend. They'd been inseparable, spending all their free time together.

Frank never suffered from depression, anger, or drug abuse. He had moved on and appeared psychologically fine. Yet he had uncontrollable and unexplained severe hypertension.

No adjective can adequately describe how terrible Frank's trauma was, given his young age, his closeness with his father, and the suddenness and brutality of the death. Yet there was an astonishing lack of serious psychological impact; Frank's remarkable resilience belied the impact of the trauma.

Frank's story does not constitute proof, but again, strongly suggests that if there is a mind-body connection in hypertension, it can be related to events that occurred decades earlier—and to the effects of overwhelming emotions that a patient is not consciously aware of.

Frank's story again demonstrates the powerful role that repression, enabling us to not feel, plays in our resilience. Yes, Frank had felt deep emotional pain at the time, but he had not fallen apart and had recovered amazingly well despite what must be considered massive trauma at a young age. He had moved on without any obvious persisting emotional impact. Instead, he developed severe, unexplained hypertension at an unusually young age.

Finally, Janice's story offers dramatic insight into the mind-body connection. It is among the most memorable and instructive in my career, and is so extraordinary and revealing, I published it as a case report in the journal *Psychosomatic Medicine*.[7]

Janice, a 43-year-old slightly overweight Black woman, had had severe hypertension since her mid-thirties. It had been inadequately controlled even though she was taking five anti-hypertensive medications. She had been hospitalized with a blood pressure of 200/130. She also had a considerable amount of protein in her urine, an indicator of injury to her kidneys from her highly elevated blood pressure.

Janice had truly uncontrollable hypertension. After having a thorough "work-up," no cause was found. There was a genetic component because everyone in her family had hypertension. But genetic hypertension is usually not this severe in one's thirties. At her current blood pressure level, complications were inevitable.

Over the next six years, Janice's blood pressure remained elevated, in the range of 155/105, despite the five medications. Some readings were as high as 200/130. She did not have "white coat" hypertension; her home readings were similarly elevated. She insisted she was taking her medication. Her pharmacist verified that she regularly refilled her prescriptions.

During these six years, there was no major stress in her life other than the uncontrolled hypertension. She had no history of psychological difficulties, and always seemed to be in a good mood. She had reluctantly left her job because of the hypertension.

Seeing me at a routine revisit, she complained that she had been suffering from a recurring nightmare every night for the previous six weeks. I asked her to describe it. In the nightmare, a man approached her from behind and attacked her. She felt him push her down and grab her. Then she would wake up screaming. For the past few weeks, she'd been sleeping in a chair, afraid to go to bed.

I almost reflexively asked if anyone had attacked her in the past. She acknowledged hesitantly that at fourteen she had been attacked and raped by someone close to her family. She had mentioned the rape only to her father. Nothing was done; the police advised him not to pursue a complaint to avoid a family scandal. Worse, Janice was hospitalized two weeks later with a severe pelvic infection that had resulted from the rape.

She did not mention the rape to anyone for the next 30 years, until our conversation. She also told me that six weeks earlier, for the first time in many years, she had met the son of the rapist and was struck by his resemblance, as an adult, to his father.

Janice was very upset. Her blood pressure in that moment was 240/150, dangerously elevated. I wanted to admit her to the hospital, but she refused. She agreed to return to my office the next day.

The next morning, she reported an excellent night's sleep, and no nightmare. Her blood pressure, to my surprise, was 120/85!

I referred Janice to a rape counselor, even though over 30 years had passed since the event. She discussed that trauma with the counselor, as well as a history of physical abuse by her ex-husband. Long-buried feelings of powerlessness, betrayal, and rage arose in those sessions.

Over the next 18 months, for the first time in many years, Janice's blood pressure remained consistently normal, averaging 126/93 on just two medications. She subsequently moved away from New York.

Janice had been destined to continue to have uncontrollable hypertension of unknown cause. And she would have been likely to suffer cardiovascular and/or renal consequences at a relatively young age.

Her description of childhood trauma was not unique among patients with severe, inadequately explained hypertension. Nor was the calmness that hid the impact of that history, from herself and from others. But Janice's story tells us that that childhood trauma is not necessarily without consequence, even in, and perhaps especially in, the most resilient among us.

As physicians we don't routinely ask about trauma that occurred decades ago or suspect that trauma from long ago could be a cause of or contributor to persisting uncontrollable hypertension or other medical conditions years or decades later. We don't routinely ask patients if they've been raped in the past, and patients don't spontaneously mention this. It would be considered invasive, and almost bizarre, to ask a new patient about a possible past rape. I had not suspected that history until Janice's nightmares led to my question.

The dramatic, persisting normalization of her uncontrollable hypertension after she gained awareness of, and disclosed, emotions that had been repressed for decades, once again led me to an inescapable conclusion: Buried emotions can persist within us and play a key, yet unsuspected causative role in severe unexplained hypertension, years or decades later. Gaining conscious awareness of those emotions can enable healing pertinent to medical illness. There was no other explanation for the rapid, substantial, and sustained easing of Janice's long-standing refractory hypertension.

I am not concluding that repression of powerful emotions plays a role in every patient with severe hypertension, or that it's the sole cause of refractory hypertension. Genetic and lifestyle factors clearly play a major role. But my experience tells me that repressed emotions, though unsuspected, underlie hypertension in many with severe resistant hypertension that otherwise defies explanation.

Unexplained Hypertension in Young Patients

The prevalence of hypertension increases with age; most people over sixty have hypertension. Most have relatively ordinary hypertension resulting from genetic predisposition and health habits. Generally, their hypertension is not a mind-body disorder.

In contrast, it is uncommon for individuals in their teens or twenties to have sustained hypertension, particularly if they are not overweight and don't have an unusually strong family history of hypertension. Their hypertension demands a search for an under-lying cause, but testing identifies a cause in few, leaving most to live with unexplained hypertension for decades and with lifelong medication of varying effectiveness.

It is important to point out that many young patients with blood pressure elevation don't actually have hypertension. They might have borderline blood pressure elevation, or a minimal elevation in systolic blood pressure that is surprisingly common among athletes. Or they might have "white coat" hypertension, with elevated blood pressure readings only at the doctor's office. However, young patients who truly have unexplained hypertension always arouse my curiosity.

Mindful of traditional mind-body beliefs, I always ask about current stress, but rarely hear anything that might explain the onset of their hypertension. However, when I started to ask questions about the past, here as well, I was surprised at the history of upheaval I uncovered in so many. I was equally surprised at the lack of persisting emotional impact that most patients reported. It struck me that these were stories I usually did not hear from young patients whose blood pressure was normal or who had borderline or white coat hypertension. For example, I noticed that a history of the loss of a parent during one's childhood was reported much more frequently among the patients whose hypertension was the real thing.

Ahmed, 34, had had severe uncontrollable hypertension since he was 16; it had caused severe kidney disease. He'd seen physicians at several medical centers and had had extensive testing that failed to identify a cause. He was on medication that targeted renal (kidney) mechanisms of hypertension.

Born in Pakistan, Ahmed had come to the U.S. at 15. His current life, professionally and personally, was not extraordinarily stressful, other than his health issue.

Given the early age of onset and the severity of his hypertension, I felt there had to be an explanation. And any mind-body cause would have to be related to circumstances that existed prior to age 16. I focused on that period in his life.

Ahmed grew up in an intact, functional family, reported no history of trauma, abuse, or anything out of the ordinary. Still wondering, I asked one final question. Sometimes it is the luck of asking the one question without which the door to understanding is not opened:

"You moved to the U.S. at 15; did you come together with your family?"

No, his parents had come five or six years earlier to get settled first.

"So, you were 9 or 10 when they came here?"

"Yes."

"Where did you live during those years?"

"I was at a boarding school."

"So when you were 9 or 10, both your parents left the country and you moved to a boarding school?"

"Yes, but I was fine. No problem."

Ahmed was telling me that at 9 he was separated from both parents. Because of the distance, he saw them perhaps once a year. I would consider this to be deep trauma for a 9-year-old. It was not the age of iPhones and Zoom. Yet he did not consider it upsetting.

I imagined that if he had had any pangs of homesickness, he would have been in a state of severe desperation. He could not "go home for the weekend" to see them. To survive emotionally, those emotions had to be repressed. Ironically, once again, his trauma was one that is not included in many childhood trauma questionnaires.

Despite the absence of another explanation, Ahmed was skeptical, especially given the absence of emotional distress attributable to the protective gift of repression. Given his story, I prescribed an alpha- and beta-blocker to target the SNS. His blood pressure normalized, again implicating the SNS as a driving force of his hypertension, and further suggesting, in a patient who was not experiencing emotional distress, the unsuspected role of repressed emotions.

It was the wrong time to dig up massive, buried wounds. But for the first time, his blood pressure was under control.

Ahmed's trauma was severe. He did not recognize it as severe because fortunately, it was devoid of the conscious emotional pain that would have been understandable and could have overwhelmed him. His non-reaction was conspicuous yet unnoticed. His story offered an explanation for his severe and otherwise inexplicable hypertension. The response of his hypertension to blood pressure medication targeting the SNS, along with the non-response to medications targeting the kidneys, further supported that explanation.

It is unclear when or if Ahmed will consciously confront that emotion, given the barrier of steel, the repression, that had been essential in enabling the 9-year-old to survive psychologically and thrive. It was not meant to easily unlock.

Unexplained Hypertension in a Sixteen-Year-Old: Solving the Mystery 50 Years Later

---

Margaret, 66, although a slim woman with a careful diet, had had hypertension that was unusual in its severity and its onset at the age of 16. Tests for a cause had been unrevealing. She'd been on a succession of drugs for decades, yet her blood pressure had never been well controlled.

Margaret was retired and living with her son and daughter-in-law, having accepted their invitation to live with them and be a grandma/caretaker for their children. To Margaret, it was the perfect job, the perfect situation. It was win-win for all three generations, and it had worked out wonderfully. These were the best days of her life, and clearly her blood pressure was not related to current stress.

Margaret had left home at 16. By 23 she was raising four children and had divorced her husband—it was simply not a good fit. There was no abuse; she was just unhappy. Those were rough years, but with the help of friends, she worked and raised the children. A second marriage brought another child and another divorce.

As far as stress, yes, she had endured the stress of two divorces, but that couldn't explain hypertension that had developed as a teenager.

I, of course, asked about her life before age 16. Margaret never knew her father. She did not get along with, and was not close with, her mother and stepfather. She readily acknowledged that she had been a brat and they didn't get along. But there was no abuse.

An ugly childhood, but enough to explain decades of hypertension that was evident by the age of 16? I asked further about her childhood.

It turned out that Margaret was not raised from birth by her mother. She had been raised by foster parents until she was seven and was then reunited with her birth mother, who was then married to her stepfather.

It sounded like a happy ending. But the details mattered. Margaret did not get along with her birth mother, whom she realized had taken her away from her foster parents to take care of her own needs.

I asked an obvious question: What had her life been like during those first seven years with her foster parents?

Wonderful. They had been wonderful, loving parents. They wanted to adopt her. Margaret considered them her true parents. But when they tried to adopt her, her birth mother, who had to be contacted in the adoption process, chose to take her back. Margaret was forced to leave the only parents she had known and loved, permanently, to live with her biological mother, a stranger who was neither warm nor kind. Did she ever see her foster parents again? Maybe twice.

Margaret felt all that was in the past. It hadn't affected her. How had she dealt with it? At the time, she had had no one to talk to about it. Her only means of emotional survival was through the gift of repression. Without her conscious realization or effort, the emotion was buried, and she moved on. Now, a grandmother, she was living the happiest days of a difficult life, but even now with continued, unexplained severe hypertension.

Margaret's story, without doubt, constituted an overwhelming trauma. Yet it would have been missed without careful questioning. And here as well, her hypertension came under control on medication targeting the SNS, again implicating painful emotion not apparent to her. For the first time, she *was talking about her trauma with her son, a history she had never shared with him.*

My experience over decades has taught me that in most young patients with unexplained, significant hypertension, there is a history of trauma or of a prolonged period of severe stress associated in most cases with repression of deeply painful emotion—a history that often goes unmentioned without careful questioning.

Repression of potentially overwhelming emotions enabled Ahmed and Margaret to move on in the face of great trauma at a young age. They were fortunate in not suffering severe, lifelong emotional consequences. However, the repressed emotional burden appears to have been the likely cause of their otherwise unexplained hypertension, which in both was detected at just 16, and in both was brought under control with medication directed at the SNS.

These two stories are extreme examples, but many other patients who develop hypertension at a young age also report pertinent, though not as dramatic, stories. Their stories tell us that we can harbor powerful repressed emotions that can affect our health. Their stories pertain to hypertension, and, as I came to realize, to other medical conditions as well. Their stories convey both the protective role of repression as well as the unrecognized potential for adverse health consequences.

These clinical observations, linking adverse childhood experiences to the onset of hypertension at a young age, are now supported by several large studies that have reported a clear association between childhood trauma or adverse events and the development of hypertension and abnormal hemodynamics in young adulthood.[8-11]

However, regarding those adverse events, the role and relevance of repressed emotions have not been studied—or even considered.

My conversations with patients convince me that childhood events affect adult health more than we realize, but that this link often goes unnoticed because of the absence, due to repression, of psychological manifestations. Also, adult patients, particularly those who have repressed considerable emotion, often fail to mention such childhood events when the medical history is obtained. The stories my patients are telling me show that childhood events can and do impact adult health and, ironically, do so perhaps especially among the most resilient of us. And as I will discuss in the next few chapters, many studies have similarly reported a link between adverse childhood events and any number of inadequately explained adult medical conditions.

Fortunately, even in the absence of emotional healing, this understanding provides guidance in selecting anti-hypertensive medications that target the SNS, particularly a combination of an alpha- and beta-blocker, that are more likely to be effective than the usual medications that target the kidneys. This response pattern further supports the likelihood that repressed emotions, though unfelt, play a major role in a large proportion of patients with hypertension that developed at a young age.

Can gaining awareness of emotions repressed since childhood enable physical healing? This question has rarely been explored or even considered. In many, the barrier is profound, and was clearly necessary, and a blessing at the time. Janice's healing experience conveyed a powerful message. However, in the absence of conscious emotional symptoms or awareness of the role of repressed emotions in our health, this potentially healing pathway will be inapparent to most. It is my hope that understanding and awareness of the role of repressed emotions might open the door to new pathways.

To summarize, truly significant hypertension at a young age is uncommon and often unexplained. The role of powerful repressed emotions has not been explored or even considered. However, several clues suggest the need to pursue this pathway:

- The history of abuse, trauma, overwhelming stress, or less dramatic but pervasive family dysfunction reported by a high proportion of patients I've seen, along with the misleading absence of overt emotional consequences

- The response to drugs that target the SNS rather than the kidneys

- Research that has documented a link between adverse child-hood experiences and blood pressure elevation at a young age

All these findings support this still rarely considered explanation for a condition that otherwise remains a lifelong mystery.

References

1. Achelrod D, Wenzel U, Frey S. Systematic review and meta-analysis of the prevalence of resistant hypertension in treated hypertensive populations. Am J Hypertens. 2015 Mar;28(3):355-61. doi: 10.1093/ajh/hpu151. Epub 2014 Aug 25. PMID: 25156625.
2. Calhoun DA, Booth JN 3rd, Oparil S, et al. Refractory hypertension: determination of prevalence, risk factors, and comorbidities in a large, population-based cohort. Hypertension. 2014

Mar;63(3):451-8. doi: 10.1161/HYPERTENSIONAHA.113.02026. Epub 2013 Dec 9. PMID: 24324035; PMCID: PMC4141646.

3. Muxfeldt ES, Chedier B. Refractory hypertension: what do we know so far? J Hum Hypertens. 2021 Mar;35(3):181-183. doi: 10.1038/s41371-020-00409-z. Epub 2020 Sep 1. PMID: 32873873.

4. Mann SJ, Gerber LM. Psychological characteristics and responses to antihypertensive drug therapy. J Clin Hypertens (Greenwich). 2002 Jan-Feb;4(1):25-34. doi: 10.1111/j.1524-6175.2002.00493.x. PMID: 11821634.

5. Mann SJ, James GD. Defensiveness and essential hypertension. J Psychosom Res. 1998 Aug;45(2):139-48. doi: 10.1016/s0022-3999(97)00293-6. PMID: 9753386.

6. Dudenbostel T, Acelajado MC, Pisoni R, Li P, Oparil S, Calhoun DA. Refractory Hypertension: Evidence of Heightened Sympathetic Activity as a Cause of Antihypertensive Treatment Failure. Hypertension. 2015 Jul;66(1):126-33. doi: 10.1161/HYPERTENSIONAHA.115.05449. Epub 2015 May 18. PMID: 25987662; PMCID: PMC4465856.

7. Mann SJ, Delon M. Improved hypertension control after disclosure of decades-old trauma. Psychosom Med. 1995 Sep-Oct;57(5):501-5. doi: 10.1097/00006842-199509000-00014. PMID: 8552743.

8. Su S, Wang X, Pollock JS, et al. Adverse childhood experiences and blood pressure trajectories from childhood to young adulthood: the Georgia stress and Heart study. Circulation. 2015 May 12;131(19):1674-81. doi: 10.1161/CIRCULATIONAHA.114.013104. Epub 2015 Apr 9. PMID: 25858196; PMCID: PMC4430378.

9. Stein DJ, Scott K, Haro Abad JM, et al. Early childhood adversity and later hypertension: data from the World Mental Health Survey. Ann Clin Psychiatry. 2010 Feb;22(1):19-28. PMID: 20196979; PMCID: PMC3486699.

10. Riley EH, Wright RJ, Jun HJ, Hibert EN, Rich-Edwards JW. Hypertension in adult survivors of child abuse: observations from the Nurses' Health Study II. J Epidemiol Community Health. 2010 May;64(5):413-8. doi: 10.1136/jech.2009.095109. PMID: 20445210; PMCID: PMC3744368.

11. Kreatsoulas C, Fleegler EW, Kubzansky LD, McGorrian CM, Subramanian SV. Young Adults and Adverse Childhood Events: A Potent Measure of Cardiovascular Risk. Am J Med. 2019 May;132(5):605-613. doi: 10.1016/j.amjmed.2018.12.022. Epub 2019 Jan 9. PMID: 30639555.

PART 2

The Upside and Downside of Repression

My observations in patients with hypertension opened my eyes to the role that repressed emotions can and do play in the mind-body connection. I subsequently observed the relevance of this understanding in other medical conditions whose causes, even today, remain incompletely understood. For example, we understand the pathophysiology of many inflammatory diseases, but we don't fully understand what triggers them. Similarly, the origin of many prominent conditions characterized by chronic pain remains a mystery.

It is time to understand that the repression of emotion, though hidden from our awareness, plays a crucial role both in our resilience and in the mind-body connection. In this manner, repression truly does have an upside and a downside.

Chapter 7

The Gift of Repression
Its Crucial Yet Unnoticed Role in Our Resilience

A t some point, most of us encounter profound stress, losses, or trauma that permanently alters our lives. When they happen, we must deal with them, and coping can be difficult. Fortunately, we have many resources to help us through those challenging periods.

Listening to many patients who successfully survived severe stress or trauma convinces me that we possess more resilience than we realize, and that repression, though unmentioned, often plays a crucial role in that resilience. Though unnoticed, this defense seemed apparent in the stories and in the resilience of so many of my patients who had survived major trauma or severe and prolonged emotional stress without suffering emotional consequences such as depression, anxiety, PTSD, or others. On a larger scale, repression plays an important role in the emotional survival of many of us as we face the harsh challenges of life. Yet, amazingly, the phenomenon of repression, and its crucial role, remains largely unrecognized.

It makes sense that evolution provided us, and had to provide us, with the gift of the capacity to not feel, to protect us from being emotionally overwhelmed. It is the most powerful defense we possess to support our emotional resilience, yet we don't realize it is operative, and to this day its role in our resilience is widely unknown.

Repression is a widely misunderstood and overlooked process. Even as it helps protect us from being emotionally incapacitated, we are unaware that it is operative. Few realize its critical role in the emotional resilience of humankind. Consideration of its role is conspicuously missing from most studies on resilience.[1] Even questionnaires created to "measure" resilience overlook the role of repression.[2] Though no technology was necessary to understand the concept of repression, it was not described until the nineteenth century. And even today, its crucial role in our resilience is rarely recognized, considered, or understood, even in discussions and books devoted to the topic of resilience.

Although repression of emotion is often spoken of as a psychological problem or is regarded as psychopathology, it is actually a built-in defense mechanism crucial to emotional resilience. In the aftermath of severe trauma, repression is not at the root of subsequent psychopathology. Emotional consequences of trauma, more often, are a result of the *failure* to repress, or to maintain repression.

We would be emotionally naked without the cocoon of resilience that repression provides. I suspect that those who repress when it is necessary to repress are the ones most likely to survive and thrive.

Studies indicate that a history of abuse or trauma can be found in anywhere from 15 to 30 percent of Americans, or even more, depending on how trauma is defined. Childhood abuse or trauma is common.[3] In a recent report, over 60 percent report having experienced at least one adverse childhood event (ACE), and over 25 percent report three or more.[4] Childhood events are clearly associated with an increased likelihood of psychological problems in adulthood, including anxiety, depression, and psychosis.[5,6]

Yet although many survivors of childhood trauma suffer emotional consequences in adulthood, many don't, and can be considered to be resilient. In my clinical practice I was surprised by how many patients had moved on in life without overt psychological sequelae from severe childhood trauma or losses, whose emotional survival was largely attributable to the blessing of repression. And they didn't just survive; they thrived. Many convey their story differently than do other trauma survivors, saying, "I put it behind me." And they moved on quickly.

In this era of the ascendance of psychology, we are taught to feel our feelings. However, some events, depending on their severity and the circumstances in our lives, are too overwhelming for most of us to deal with and, at the same time, function normally. This is particularly true in childhood, and particularly in the absence of adequate emotional support. Here, repression is crucial, and is a true gift to many. Emotional survival achieved by *not* feeling emotions, and *not* talking about them! Frankly, we suffer psychologically if we cannot repress when we need to.

In dealing with extremely stressful events, being "tough," being resilient, can be understood in two ways. It can mean experiencing and dealing with severely painful emotions and eventually healing and moving on. Or it can mean the opposite: repressing, not feeling, and moving on. Many resilient individuals deal consciously with painful emotions linked to severe stress or trauma and heal. It is optimal if we can confront those emotions in this manner. However, my patients' stories have conveyed that in dealing with severe stress or trauma, with emotional distress that could challenge our capacity to consciously cope, the best option often lies in our ability to not feel.

The patients whose stories indicate repression of overwhelming emotion never consciously "decided" to block off that emotion; it was their unconscious mind that, remarkably, without conscious effort or awareness, kept, and in many still keeps, those emotions hidden.

Ideally, when the threat to emotional and/or physical survival has passed, conscious emotional healing is possible. However, there are barriers to healing. In most, the opportunity for healing goes unnoticed because of our lack of awareness of the burden of repressed emotions. For many, a lifelong partitioning of emotion through repression might remain the best path. As discussed here, the reaction of the patient, or reader, is perhaps the best guide of the path to be taken.

Conscious and Unconscious Defenses

Given our ability to repress, why then do so many suffer psychologically? Clearly, we don't repress all emotion, and being able to repress does not provide an emotion-free life. Our conscious and unconscious mechanisms shield us, but do not protect all of us all the time.

We fortunately possess both conscious and unconscious defenses that enable us to withstand stress and trauma. We are psychologically healthiest when we can use both: consciously face and deal with emotions related to day-to-day stress—even severe stress—and to repress that which would overwhelm us emotionally.

Our Conscious Defenses

Innumerable books have been written about the conscious defenses that help us deal with stress and potentially traumatic events. Our ability to feel and tolerate emotional pain is determined largely by genetics, childhood experience, and current circumstances. It is strongly linked to factors such as connectedness with others, support from family and friends, spiritual faith, and community. And the passage of time is crucial in allowing us to gradually heal.

Our ability to consciously suppress painful emotions helps us function. Our will to endure is buttressed by a sense of purpose. Also crucial is an awareness of gratitude: our ability to be mindful of our many blessings. We also have tools, including relaxation techniques, meditation, and psychotherapy. We have the beauty and penetration of music, and the pets that surround us with innocence and love. And, of course, medications that are truly miraculous in tamping down, when needed, distressful emotions.

These are all foot soldiers of resilience.

However, while noting the many important conscious tools that support our resilience, I sometimes wonder whether, in recent generations, we are evolving toward decreasing resilience. I notice the prevalence of problems such as anxiety and depression, the prominent role of psychologists, and the widespread use of anti-anxiety and other psychotropic drugs. And this is occurring in an era when modern technology has improved day-to-day living conditions.

We are also losing some bulwarks of resilience as we witness the decline in religious faith, the loss of community, the anonymity of living in a large metropolis, and the prevalence of smaller and more geographically separated families. Although theoretically there is no limit to the supply of connectedness, too often, and for many reasons, we live lives with a scarcity of connectedness.

We also lack confidence in our ability to tolerate severely painful emotions and heal. Our emotional pain is greatly magnified by the fear that we will not recover emotionally; we fail to realize that we have more resilience than we think we do.

Another underutilized resource is the power of reassurance. Reassuring words communicated by a physician, member of the clergy, psychologist, friend, or family member, spoken genuinely rather than as a "technique," have a considerable impact. Yet too often, the necessary words and sentiment are not spoken by those in a position to offer them; we don't realize the impact these words can have.

Our Unconscious Defenses

Much less is written about the unconscious defenses that, temporarily or permanently, keep potentially overwhelming emotion out of our awareness. Few realize that often, our most powerful emotions are not those we are aware of, the ones that trouble us, and that mind-body research focuses on. Many times, they are the emotions that of necessity were repressed and linger beneath our conscious awareness.

Incredibly, although repression is often at the heart of our resilience, it is operative without our awareness or conscious effort.

When we repress emotions, we are not aware of them—and are unaware that we are repressing them. We take it for granted that we don't feel emotional distress.

We are fortunate in that repression is built into us. It is programmed into us and serves billions of people, yet almost no one is aware it is operative.

I believe repression is employed as an emotional defense far more commonly than is realized, perhaps at times by most of us. Without realizing it, repression serves us, helping us to avoid being overwhelmed.

The understanding to which this book is dedicated, first and foremost, is that in patients who have survived trauma through repression, our unconscious mind provided exactly what we needed. Repression of overwhelming emotion during or in the aftermath of severe stress or trauma is *not* psychopathology; it is a cornerstone of resilience.

The Term "Repression"

There are many challenges in the discussion of repression. The term "repression" means different things to different people, even among psychologists, hampering more widespread understanding of its overlooked yet crucial role in emotional health, resilience, and illness. Is it a conscious or unconscious process? Do repressed emotions persist, hidden in our unconscious? And do those emotions, unbeknownst to us, eventually affect us emotionally or physically?

There are many reasons for this confusion. The confusion starts with the many interpretations of the concept of repression. The number of terms used to describe repression attests to the lack of consensus about the term's meaning. Also, the study of unconscious mechanisms is extremely challenging. Some say it's time to put the theory of repression behind us and move on. These challenges, however, don't disprove the essential role of repression in our psyche.

Terms that have been used to describe repression include "intentional non-thinking" that leads to forgetting; "thought inhibition"; "selective inattention"; "cognitive avoidance"; and "motivated forgetting." These terms are not specifically indicative of unconscious mechanisms. Other terms regarding avoidance of unwanted emotions include isolation, denial, rationalization, projection, reaction formation, intellectualization, dissociation, sublimation, and more.

Repression has been described as an unconscious process.[7] However, many contemporary authors avoid any distinction between the conscious and the unconscious.[8]

My strong belief, after years of clinical observations, is that repression is an unconscious process. For the sake of clarity in discussion, in this book I am defining and using the term repression as follows:

A process that operates without conscious intention, effort, or awareness to keep threatening or overwhelming emotion out of awareness. We don't consciously decide to block painful emotions from our awareness; repression is driven by our unconscious mind. When we are repressing emotions, we are not aware that we are repressing them, or that they linger within us.

Clarifying Three Terms
Denial, Suppression, and Repression

In discussing repression, it is vital to differentiate three different terms that are often confused with each other: *denial, suppression*, and *repression*.

Repression vs. Denial
Denial is a fascinating process by which we avoid distress by denying the reality of our situation. The expression that someone is "in denial" is widely used. It is considered a more primitive defense than repression in that it denies reality.

For example, a patient, after being informed of a terminal diagnosis, is certain the diagnosis is wrong, no matter how clear the evidence. He is not distressed because, strangely, he doesn't see the reality that is obvious to everyone around him. This reduces emotional distress, but requires detachment from reality, from the facts. Denial can reduce our distress but stands in the way of taking necessary actions.

With *repression,* one is not in *denial* of the facts. One acknowledges reality, but does not feel, and is unaware of, the severe, painful emotion that could be expected. For example, being able to move on without grief or sadness after the death of a loved one.

Although denial of reality is clearly problematic in the long term, I would add that sometimes even denial can serve us. For example, when our immediate reality is crushing, a temporary escape from reality is not always a bad thing. As bad as it sounds, part of resilience might sometimes involve avoiding reality. Our unconscious ability to separate ourselves from a terrifying reality when there is nothing we can do in the moment might actually be protecting us from breakdown.

Even psychosis, a separation from reality that usually is of great concern, sometimes can serve to protect us from reality at the time of a huge crisis. For example, there is a state of mind called "ICU psychosis" (also called delirium) in which patients, particularly when hospitalized in the intensive care unit, become psychotic. It is usually temporary. When it occurs, patients are sometimes treated with antipsychotic drugs.

I suspect, however, that sometimes ICU psychosis is a protective event. Being in an ICU with tubes in every orifice, hearing bells and alarms, feeling sick and frightened, having no conception of day or night and with no action that one can take in the moment, must be a terrifying experience. In this setting, an escape from that reality might serve to help a patient avoid panic. If a patient is not violent, is not trying to escape the bed or unit, is cooperating with treatment, and is comfortably lying in bed in a made-up reality, perhaps this is exactly what he or she needs to do.

I remember a patient of mine who was in an ICU in New York City who thought he was in Hawaii. Rather than correct him and thereby remind him of his circumstances in the moment, I asked how he was enjoying the weather, and we had a pleasant conversation. The next day, a little further along in his recovery, he was back to reality.

Another means of avoiding painful reality, ironically, is the firm belief in a fantasy. I remember a 40-year-old patient who told me that his father had died when he was seven. When I asked how he had coped, he said that for years he believed his father was going to come back. Incompatible with reality? Yes. But depending on the circumstances in which it occurs, if a harmless false belief, a fantasy, can provide comfort for a suddenly orphaned seven-year-old, then I would consider it a helpful coping mechanism.

Repression vs. Suppression

Many use the terms *"suppress"* and *"repress"* interchangeably, resulting in confusion. But they have very different meanings. Understanding the distinction between the two is crucial to understanding human resilience. I believe the following definitions offer clarity in distinguishing them:

Suppression is a familiar conscious process by which we try to keep painful emotions out of our awareness, for example, by diverting our attention to other things, through willpower or keeping busy. It is a valuable part of our resilience. We all make *conscious* efforts to avoid, or *suppress*, painful emotions. And when we are trying to suppress emotions, we know we are doing so.

Suppression is an effective defense mechanism that helps us get through stressful periods and put aside painful emotions, and it enables us to function without being continuously distressed. When we are grieving, for example, we often rely on suppressing emotional pain by keeping busy.

With *repression*, in contrast, emotions are blocked from our awareness without conscious effort, and without our awareness that we are repressing them. It is as if we are on autopilot—without any effort, we simply don't feel the emotional pain. And repression can continue for decades—even a lifetime.

To put it simply into an example:

Repression: I know I have cancer and am going to die, but I'm not upset.

Denial: I've been told I have cancer, but I know the tests are wrong.

Suppression: I know I have cancer, but I'll focus, as much as possible, on other things and try not to let my fear of dying dominate my remaining time.

It is not surprising that repressed emotions and their effects on our health are not widely recognized. When we repress emotions, we don't know we are repressing them. We don't know that we harbor those unfelt emotions. Should someone suggest that we are repressing painful emotions, we can't see it, and are likely to insist there is no emotion. That's why the role of repressing emotion can be discerned only by looking beneath the words of the story and considering the role of the missing emotions.

In understanding repression, a crucial question must be considered: In the aftermath of trauma, can we feel emotional pain and at the same time repress other emotions? My impression is yes, one can feel and be aware of some degree of emotional distress, yet also repress and be unaware of that which would be truly overwhelming.

Ideally, conscious and unconscious defenses are interwoven in our resilience. I believe the process of grieving provides a good example of this. Repression helps us titrate the distress of grieving, allowing us time and protecting us from being overwhelmed by intolerable or relentless distress, and enabling us to function. There are times when pain sears us; these are the times when we are doing the work of grieving until, as we heal, the pain eventually begins to ease and become more tolerable. But we could not function during the grieving process if we were overwhelmed by the emotional pain all day, every day.

Some of the time, we consciously *suppress* our emotional pain, to keep it out of mind. We occupy our attention with other things. At other times, without conscious effort, and without realizing it, we *repress* the emotions, giving us a welcome break from the difficult work of grieving, and allowing us to recover over time. At those times we can be amazed that we feel very well, as if nothing had happened, even though reality did not change. That is repression. A gift.

Repressed Memories

Many confuse the notion of repressed emotions with that of repressed memories. In my experience, patients who have repressed crushing emotions do recall the abuse, trauma, or events that led to the repression. It is the emotions related to those memories that are repressed.

There is considerable controversy about repressed memories, and the veracity of recovered memories, such as the recovered memories of sexual abuse during childhood.[9] I suspect the answer lies somewhere in the middle; in some cases, the repressed memories that arise reflect events that did happen. I want to be clear, though, that this book is about repression of emotions, not memories.

References:

1. Poole JC, Dobson KS, Pusch D. Childhood adversity and adult depression: The protective role of psychological resilience. Child Abuse Negl. 2017 Feb;64:89-100. doi: 10.1016/j.chiabu.2016.12.012. Epub 2017 Jan 2. PMID: 28056359.

2. Campbell-Sills L, Stein MB. Psychometric analysis and refinement of the Connor-davidson Resilience Scale (CD-RISC): Validation of a 10-item measure of resilience. J Trauma Stress. 2007 Dec;20(6):1019-28. doi: 10.1002/jts.20271. PMID: 18157881.

3. De Bellis MD, Zisk A. The biological effects of childhood trauma. Child Adolesc Psychiatr Clin N Am. 2014 Apr;23(2):185-222, vii. doi: 10.1016/j.chc.2014.01.002. Epub 2014 Feb 16. PMID: 24656576; PMCID: PMC3968319.

4. Hustedde C. Adverse Childhood Experiences. Prim Care. 2021 Sep;48(3):493-504. doi: 10.1016/j.pop.2021.05.005. Epub 2021 Jul 10. PMID: 34311853.

5. Vila-Badia R, Butjosa A, Del Cacho N, et al. Types, prevalence and gender differences of childhood trauma in first-episode psychosis. What is the evidence that childhood trauma is related to symptoms and functional outcomes in first episode psychosis? A systematic review. Schizophr Res. 2021 Feb;228:159-179. doi: 10.1016/j.schres.2020.11.047. Epub 2021 Jan 10. PMID: 33434728.

6. Kuzminskaite E, Penninx BWJH, van Harmelen AL, Elzinga BM, Hovens JGFM, Vinkers CH. Childhood Trauma in Adult Depressive and Anxiety Disorders: An Integrated Review on Psychological and Biological Mechanisms in the NESDA Cohort. J Affect Disord. 2021 Mar 15;283:179-191. doi: 10.1016/j.jad.2021.01.054. Epub 2021 Jan 28. PMID: 33561798.

7. Jones BP. Repression: the evolution of a psychoanalytic concept from the 1890s to the 1990s. J Am Psychoanal Assoc. 1993;41(1):63-93. doi: 10.1177/000306519304100103. PMID: 8426058.

8. Garssen B. Repression: finding our way in the maze of concepts. J Behav Med. 2007 Dec;30(6):471-81. doi: 10.1007/s10865-007-9122-7. Epub 2007 Jul 25. PMID: 17653842; PMCID: PMC2080858

9. Otgaar H, Howe ML, Patihis L, et al, The Return of the Repressed: The Persistent and Problematic Claims of Long-Forgotten Trauma. Perspect Psychol Sci. 2019;14(6):1072-1095. doi:10.1177/1745691619862306.

Chapter 8

Connectedness, Faith, Repression, and Resilience
Two Special Patients

As a physician I have had the privilege of meeting and having intimate conversations with many amazing people. I am moved by, and remember well, the stories of many. In this chapter I wanted to tell the stories of two patients—stories that powerfully convey the resilience with which we are endowed. I could not witness their remarkable stories without pondering the key role of resources such as connectedness, faith, and repression, and the mixture of conscious and unconscious components woven into human resilience. Their stories touched me and have been etched into my memory. I want to convey my amazement.

Clearly, many live lives that are troubled, or shattered, by adversity and a lack of resilience. Overcoming adversity is a battle we all face, to one extent or another. Many books have been written about the tools of resilience that can help us, but with our limitations, resilience is not universal. In this book I am focusing on resilience, and the harm we experience when we underestimate our resilience. However, human frailty is also a reality. We can try to buttress our resilience, but there are no guarantees.

I have been fortunate enough to meet and interact with patients whose resilience persisted through unending, lifelong stress. The stories of two patients whose resilience was beyond anything I could imagine are particularly memorable to me. They were severely disabled yet managed to avoid the painful sadness that could easily have dominated their lives. I was so touched by their strength that, in a book about resilience, I could not resist the urge to share their stories.

My Strongest Patient: Faith and Resilience

Rosemary (her real name) was 70. She suffered from muscular dystrophy that presented when she was 21, just as she was emerging into adulthood. She had been a nursing student and was engaged to be married. Both of those pursuits ended. Her life since then had been spent in a bed or in a wheelchair, and she was attached for decades to a ventilator. Fortunately, she was able to communicate quite well by blurting out several words in between inhalations.

The first thing one noticed about Rosemary was her disability. It was impossible to not see. The next thing one noticed, and could not miss, was her spirit. She was content, perhaps even happy. She conveyed needs, but never complaints. To use the cliché, she recognized the hand she was dealt and celebrated what she had rather than complain about what she didn't have. She was also very verbal in conveying her gratitude. She never failed to convey heartfelt gratitude for what she had.

Rosemary was delightful to be with. She raised issues, but not in a complaining way, though she undoubtedly had a litany of hardships that had dominated her life for decades and would continue to do so. There was no hope of improvement. Her life was, of course, dominated by her disabilities and medical condition. Yet as much as possible, she avoided living life as a patient rather than as a person.

Rosemary had had many hospital admissions for respiratory and other problems. While she was in the hospital after urologic surgery, I took the time to chat at length with her. I acknowledged the hardship of the surgery and conveyed to her that I admired her strength. She appreciated the recognition, and my awareness that despite her brave front, I knew how tough life was for her. A tear rolled down her cheek. She described how having God with her had strengthened her. I asked how she had come to her strength.

Rosemary's muscle strength began to deteriorate when she was 21, and it deteriorated quickly. She was depressed. Although always religious, she was angry at God. Her career and marital plans fell apart. During those early years, she went to a quiet retreat at Our Lady of Lourdes in France. After two or three days she experienced a major shift, a transformation. Instead of being weighed down and tormented by her condition, she accepted it, and felt connected to God; she felt God within her. With that, she felt she had everything she needed. That connection gave her strength, and she fought to keep it. She sometimes lost the connection, but she would focus within and *get it back. She remained content with what she had during all the years since then, connected to God within her.*

I'll never forget her phrase: "I have everything I need to be happy." Her faith did not change her disability—it transformed her experience of it.

I saw Rosemary as having had an amazing ability to repress, to not feel that which was intolerable, an ability nurtured by the power of her faith. She knew the desperation and hopelessness of her situation, but she didn't feel it.

Rosemary died in her 70s, after living half a century with her disability. I have never encountered anyone more resilient than Rosemary, who demonstrated to me, more than any other patient, the power of faith.

Rosemary's astounding resilience raises a question I can't answer: Does the power of faith underlie our ability to consciously tolerate and minimize chronic, overwhelming emotional distress? Or does it buttress our ability to successfully repress it? Or both? I don't know, but regardless, I suspect that today's decline in faith is a development that weakens resilience in a tough world.

The Power of Love and Connectedness

The power of connectedness requires both the ability to experience connectedness and the availability of someone with whom to connect.

I met Kevin only once, when he was 60. He had been hospitalized due to heart failure and had developed sepsis, a bacterial bloodstream infection. I was asked to see him regarding his blood pressure, which tended to fluctuate severely. We discussed treatment options then talked for about another half-hour. Two days later he developed septic shock and died.

During his second day in septic shock, when he was unresponsive, on a ventilator, I also met, for the only time, his wife and daughters. They looked grim. We stood in the hall outside the ICU and talked.

Kevin, once a high school football star, had suffered a broken neck while playing football when he was 16. It left him a paraplegic, unable to walk, and with partial use of his arms. Barbara had met and begun dating him before the injury, which did not dissuade her from marrying him. She told me of Kevin's ability to deny emotion, to claim he was happy though he was permanently paralyzed, was frequently in pain, and had experienced numerous medical complications over the years. He was not one to bemoan his fate. If anything, he proclaimed that he was happy despite all.

I sensed his family's admiration of this very special man. Walking away, I was moved. I sensed the love in the family and the loveliness of Kevin's wife and daughters. I realized that it was not just Kevin's attitude that saw him through. It was the deeply felt love he was surrounded by. It was not just a victory driven by Kevin's awesome spirit; it was a demonstration of the power of love and connectedness that had permeated their home, a love that was powerfully obvious.

Despite all, Kevin had had a happy life, one surrounded by more love than that of almost any patient I've ever met.

One cannot hear the deeply personal stories of so many patients over decades of medical practice and not be astonished at the human capacity for resilience. Their stories also led me to appreciate the mixture of conscious and unconscious resources interwoven in our resilience, and the challenge of recognizing the unnoticed, yet powerful unconscious component that secretly strengthens that resilience.

Thank you, Rosemary, and thank you, Kevin, for being my teachers.

Chapter 9

Two Types of Repression

S*tudies on repression*, along with decades of clinical experience, suggest that two forms of repression are relevant
to the mind-body connection. One is the repression of emotions
related to a history of trauma, abuse, or periods of enormous
stress. The other is often referred to as a "repressive coping style,"
the tendency, in the absence of a history of trauma, to go through
life without feeling the emotional distress most others feel. These
are people we might call very "even-keeled," who seem inoculated
against feeling emotional distress.

In this chapter I will discuss these two forms of repression.

Repression in Coping with Trauma

Many articles and books have been written about the persisting psychological sequelae of abuse or trauma, and the medications and therapies
helpful in dealing with them. Abuse or trauma can confront us at any
age, during childhood or adulthood, and with considerable impact.

Although I've observed the impact of past trauma in many patients, what strikes me more are the many patients I encounter who have put past trauma behind them and have moved on, seemingly with no overt lingering psychological effects, and without having seen a psychologist or psychiatrist. I am struck by their considerable resilience, which is likely due, at least in part, to repression. I suspect that psychiatrists and psychologists write less about this because they are less likely to see these successful survivors.

Studies report that resilience in the face of potentially traumatic events is not limited to a small proportion of the population as many have believed. Bonanno reported that a large proportion of us, 35 to 65 percent, are resilient.[1]

Studies of Post-Traumatic Stress Disorder (PTSD) similarly convey that resilience in the face of trauma is common. The development of PTSD is observed in 5 to 10 percent of individuals exposed to major trauma and in 28 percent of those exposed to prolonged or severe traumatic stress, for example, in veterans with severe combat exposure.[2,3] However, here as well, what interests me more is the larger proportion of trauma survivors who don't develop PTSD, and who do well with no psychological intervention.

What enabled them to endure and to thrive afterward? The origin of their resilience is at the heart of how we survive psychologically when life hits us hard. There is ample evidence that repression, at an unconscious level, is protective against PTSD in trauma survivors.[4] Similarly, a repressive coping style has been reported to be protective against Acute Stress Disorder or PTSD in the aftermath of bereavement.[5]

It is important to realize, however, that repressed emotions, though unfelt, do persist beneath conscious awareness. In some people, even years or decades later, weakening of that barrier can occur, and with it, manifestations such as unexplained anxiety or PTSD.

Yes, we can experience painful emotion at the time of trauma, and yet repress the most severe emotion. The child who suffers the sudden death of a deeply loved parent might cry for a few days and move on—not because that was sufficient to heal, but because the fiercest of the emotions were repressed, allowing the child to move forward with his or her life. The brevity of the severe emotional pain is an indicator of repression.

Repression is operative much more than we realize. It helps us buy time, enabling us to experience emotions at a pace we can tolerate. And it is also crucial to us when we must repress, temporarily or permanently, that which we cannot tolerate. For many, being "not in touch" may be the best means we have to maintain mental health, the opposite of today's emphasis on the importance of feeling our emotions.

Repressive Coping Style
Repression in Dealing with Day-to-Day Stress

We all encounter even-keeled people who rarely get upset about the stuff that gets to most of us. We admire people who generally face adversity without getting upset, angry, or depressed. Some seem to always be "up," as was Jim (Ch. 3). Research psychologists have termed this a "repressive coping style," a pattern of dealing with emotional stress by not feeling it. In many, it is a lifelong coping style.

It is important to differentiate calmness due to a repressive coping style from calmness that reflects a calm nature and a tendency to not get bent out of shape over the little things. A repressive coping style involves also not feeling distressed over the big things either. When I ask a patient with a repressive coping style if they ever feel anxious or depressed, the response is typically "never"—no matter how much stress they have endured.

My experience suggests that being unaware of disturbing emotions is a result of repression that is rooted in, and entirely driven by, unconscious mechanisms. Patients are not failing to report having experienced feelings of depression or anxiety or anger. They truly didn't feel them.

What underlies a person's tendency to handle stress this way? Could it be a result of growing up in a family that never discussed or shared feelings or emotional pain? Or a family with a macho philosophy about not yielding to emotional pain? Or one with little connectedness or emotional support? Or a difficult or abusive family environment in which shutting down emotionally was perhaps the only path available? Or could it be the opposite: growing up in a home with a supportive and positive atmosphere that nurtures our conscious resilience? These questions have not been clearly answered, and, to a large extent, have not even been asked.

One can learn even at an early age to not feel. Lack of awareness of emotion becomes a path of survival and a habit. One becomes unaware of emotion, and *unaware of being unaware*. Life was never experienced any other way.

It is also likely that a repressive coping style is to some extent a genetically determined trait, independent of childhood circumstances. Jim, who was the "breath of fresh air" in his family, differed from his siblings despite being raised by the same parents. Some people are wired from birth to repress, and to be unaware of painful feelings. They are naturally even-keeled—or incurably optimistic. The bottom line? A repressive coping style could be a result of any number of factors.

A repressive coping style is not necessarily a bad thing. It can be viewed as a gift of evolution that helps us in coping with severe life stress, and serves as an important inborn contributor to emotional resilience. It enables one to keep a steady temper, even when coping with considerable stress or traumatic events.[5-7] And a repressive coping style has been associated with a reduced likelihood of developing psychiatric disorders.[8]

The fact that those with a repressive coping style don't focus on the negative would not seem to be a problem. The problem may lie more in those of us who focus too much on the negative and suffer emotionally.

A key problem in studying the impact of a repressive coping style is how to define and measure it. How does one measure the absence of emotion? How do we differentiate a tendency to be calm during adversity from a "repressive coping style"?

In my experience, a repressive coping style is sometimes, but not always, evident when listening to a patient. The patient "never" feels depressed or anxious, no matter the amount of stress in his or her life, past or present.

In studies, questionnaires have been used to systematically identify individuals with a repressive coping style. A means of measurement used in many studies defines a repressive coping style by scores on a pair of questionnaires: a score below the midpoint on an anxiety scale along with a score above the midpoint on a "defensiveness" scale, the Marlow-Crowne Scale, also termed a "Scale of Social Desirability."[9,10]

These questionnaires are not utilized in clinical practice. Also, they have important limitations. A discussion of their strengths and weaknesses in identifying a repressive coping style would be quite technical and beyond the scope of this book.

References:

1. Bonanno GA, Westphal M, Mancini AD. Resilience to loss and potential trauma. Annu Rev Clin Psychol. 2011;7:511-35. doi: 10.1146/annurev-clinpsy-032210-104526. PMID: 21091190.
2. Kessler RC, Sonnega A, Bromet E, Hughes M, Nelson CB. Posttraumatic stress disorder in the National Comorbidity Survey. Arch Gen Psychiatry. 1995 Dec;52(12):1048-60. doi: 10.1001/archpsyc.1995.03950240066012. PMID: 7492257.
3. Dohrenwend BP, Turner JB, Turse NA, Adams BG, Koenen KC, Marshall R. The psychological risks of Vietnam for U.S. veterans: a revisit with new data and methods. Science. 2006 Aug 18;313(5789):979-82. doi: 10.1126/science.1128944. PMID: 16917066; PMC: PMC1584215.
4. Boscarino JA, Figley CR. The Impact of Repression, Hostility, and Post-Traumatic Stress Disorder on All-Cause Mortality: A Prospective 16-Year Follow-up Study. J Nerv Ment Dis. 2009 Jun;197(6):461-6. doi: 10.1097/NMD.0b013e3181a61f3e. PMID: 19525749; PMCID: PMC3651584.
5. Coifman KG, Bonanno GA, Ray RD, Gross JJ. Does repressive coping promote resilience? Affective-autonomic response discrepancy during bereavement. J Pers Soc Psychol. 2007 Apr;92(4):745-58. doi: 10.1037/0022-3514.92.4.745. PMID: 17469956.
6. Bonanno GA, Keltner D, Holen A, Horowitz MJ. When avoiding unpleasant emotions might not be such a bad thing: verbal-autonomic response dissociation and midlife conjugal bereavement. J Pers Soc Psychol. 1995 Nov;69(5):975-89. doi: 10.1037//0022-3514.69.5.975. PMID: 7473042.

7. Prasertsri N, Holden J, Keefe FJ, Wilkie DJ. Repressive coping style: relationships with depression, pain, and pain coping strategies in lung cancer outpatients. Lung Cancer. 2011 Feb;71(2):235-40. doi: 10.1016/j.lungcan.2010.05.009. Epub 2010 Jun 16. PMID: 20557973; PMCID: PMC2980802.

8. Lane RD, Merikangas KR, Schwartz GE, Huang SS, Prusoff BA. Inverse relationship between defensiveness and lifetime prevalence of psychiatric disorder. Am J Psychiatry. 1990 May;147(5):573-8. doi: 10.1176/ajp.147.5.573. PMID: 2327485.

9. Crowne, D. P., & Marlowe, D. The approval motive: Studies in evaluative dependence. New York: Wiley, 1964.

10. Weinberger DA, Schwartz GE, Davidson RJ. Low-anxious, high-anxious, and repressive coping styles: psychometric patterns and behavioral and physiological responses to stress. J Abnorm Psychol. 1979 Aug;88(4):369-80. doi: 10.1037//0021-843x.88.4.369. PMID: 479459.

Chapter 10

The Downside of Repression

Though rarely recognized, the ability to repress painful and
potentially overwhelming emotion is clearly beneficial
and essential to human emotional survival. That is why evolution
would favor our ability to repress.

Repression clearly has an upside that is not widely appreciated.
However, equally unrecognized, it also has a downside. Evidence
from published studies, and my experience with patients that is
congruent with the results of those studies, indicate that the burden
of repressed emotions is also associated with an increased risk of
harmful medical consequences. In this way, our genetically favored
ability to repress emotions is a mixed blessing. That should not be
surprising. Many genes favored by evolution can similarly have a
downside. Here are a couple of obvious examples.

Throughout the long history of human life on Earth, the scarcity
of food has been a threat to survival. Those who were genetically
programmed to utilize their caloric intake more efficiently were
able to survive with less food and fewer calories, and were less

likely than others to die of starvation. Today, those survival genes are called obesity genes; they are contributory to the widespread public health problem of obesity.

Similarly, in populations living in hot climates and consuming a natural diet, the low salt content of that natural diet put them at risk of dehydration. Genes that reduce the loss of sodium in urine protected against death from dehydration. However, today, with the high salt content of processed foods, and particularly in more temperate climates, those same genes are now considered a cause of salt-sensitive hypertension.

In both instances, genes that conferred a survival advantage are now viewed as harmful genes that are contributory to obesity and hypertension. Evolution didn't go wrong; it was the change in the environment that altered the genes' effect from one of increased survival to one of harm. Evolution was concerned with enabling us to survive and procreate. Our health and survival beyond our forties and fifties was never its concern.

In accord with these analogies, the ability to repress emotions, whether in the context of major stress or as a repressive coping style, can and should be viewed as a survival advantage in a world where humanity faces enormous emotional challenges. It is associated with a reduction in psychological distress and the prevention of psychiatric illness. However, the burden of repressed emotions, though unfelt, persists within us. And the emotions we have repressed, though we are unaware of them and would legitimately insist that we don't feel, can be far more powerful than the emotions we do experience and focus on.

Though a gift, our genetically conferred ability to repress and maintain within us a burden of unfelt emotions can ultimately affect our health, with physical manifestations that medical science cannot otherwise fully explain. That cost, however, remains hidden from the annals of medicine because mind-body research has focused almost exclusively on our day-to-day stress and emotional distress.

Trauma survivors who have thrived by virtue of having repressed potentially overpowering emotions are unaware of those emotions and would insist they don't exist. Nor are they aware that they have repressed them for decades—or for a lifetime. Repressed emotions, however, though unfelt, do persist within. And, ultimately, they can affect us medically more than the day-to-day emotions we do experience.

My clinical experience, as discussed in the coming chapters, indicates that the burden of repressed emotions leaves a legacy as an unsuspected factor in medical and emotional conditions whose cause is otherwise unclear. Ironically, if those conditions become evident at a time when life circumstances are stable, we are unlikely to suspect a mind-body link.

Repressed Emotions and the Mind-Body Link

Although only a small proportion of mind-body studies have examined the role of repression, research has documented a link between a repressive coping style and several medical conditions. It is linked to increased blood pressure reactivity and hypertension.[1-4] And studies indicate that several prevalent conditions, including coronary heart disease, cancer, and asthma, are associated with adverse childhood experiences and with a repressive coping style.[5-11]

As discussed in this book, studies suggest that repression of emotion can contribute to certain forms of hypertension, to pain and fatigue syndromes, and to conditions such as colitis, migraine, chronic pain disorders, and likely other conditions that otherwise remain inadequately explained.

The impact of the burden of repressed emotions thus appears to be considerable, yet is rarely recognized. In the coming chapters I will explore its unrecognized impact on health.

References

1. Gleiberman L. Repressive/defensive coping, blood pressure, and cardiovascular rehabilitation. Curr Hypertens Rep. 2007 Mar;9(1):7-12. doi: 10.1007/s11906-007-0003-9. PMID: 17362665.

2. King AC, Taylor CB, Albright CA, Haskell WL. The relationship between repressive and defensive coping styles and blood pressure responses in healthy, middle-aged men and women. J Psychosom Res. 1990;34(4):461-71. doi: 10.1016/0022-3999(90)90070-k. PMID: 2376846.

3. Rutledge T, Linden W. Defensiveness and 3-year blood pressure levels among young adults: the mediating effect of stress-reactivity. Ann Behav Med. 2003 Winter;25(1):34-40. doi: 10.1207/S15324796ABM2501_05. PMID: 12581934.

4. Grossman P, Watkins LL, Ristuccia H, Wilhelm FH. Blood pressure responses to mental stress in emotionally defensive patients with stable coronary artery disease. Am J Cardiol. 1997 Aug 1;80(3):343-6. doi: 10.1016/s0002-9149(97)00359-7. PMID: 9264432.

5. Denollet J, Martens EJ, Nyklícek I, Conraads VM, de Gelder B. Clinical events in coronary patients who report low distress: adverse effect of repressive coping. Health Psychol. 2008 May;27(3):302-8. doi: 10.1037/0278-6133.27.3.302. PMID: 18624593.

6. Felitti VJ, Anda RF, Nordenberg D, et al. Relationship of childhood abuse and household dysfunction to many of the leading causes of death in adults. The Adverse Childhood Experiences (ACE) Study. Am J Prev

Med. 1998 May;14(4):245-58. doi: 10.1016/s0749-3797(98)00017-8. PMID: 9635069.

7. Dong M, Giles WH, Felitti VJ, et al. Insights into causal pathways for ischemic heart disease: adverse childhood experiences study. Circulation. 2004 Sep 28;110(13):1761-6. doi: 10.1161/01. CIR.0000143074.54995.7F. Epub 2004 Sep 20. PMID: 15381652.

8. Feldman JM, Lehrer PM, Hochron SM, Schwartz GE. Defensiveness and individual response stereotypy in asthma. Psychosom Med. 2002 Mar-Apr;64(2):294-301. doi: 10.1097/00006842-200203000-00013. PMID: 11914446; PMCID: PMC2958692.

9. Wainwright NW, Surtees PG, Wareham NJ, Harrison BD. Psychosocial factors and asthma in a community sample of older adults. J Psychosom Res. 2007 Mar;62(3):357-61. doi: 10.1016/j.jpsychores.2006.10.013. PMID: 17324687

10. Jensen M.R. (1987). Psychobiological factors predicting the course of breast cancer. Journal of personality, 55(2), 317-342. doi: 10.1111/j.1467-6494.1987.tb00439.

11. Watson M, Pettingale KW, Greer S. Emotional control and autonomic arousal in breast cancer patients. J Psychosom Res. 1984;28(6):467-74. doi: 10.1016/0022-3999(84)90080-1. PMID: 6520802.

PART 3

Repressed Emotions and Other Chronic Medical Conditions

In medicine, we encounter many common conditions whose underlying cause remains inadequately understood. We have medications that can ameliorate symptoms or inflammation in many of those conditions, but we still lack a cure for most of them.

To date, there is a lack of awareness of, or studies concerning, a possible link between repressed emotions and medical illnesses. And since patients who are not suffering emotional distress don't seek psychological counseling, clinical psychologists are also unlikely to write about this unexplored link.

My observations in patients with hypertension raise an important question: Is this understanding of the role of

repressed emotions relevant as well to other highly prevalent medical conditions whose cause, despite decades of research, remains unclear. Conditions where decades of mind-body research that has focused on day-to-day stress and emotional distress have provided scant insight.

My experience suggests that here as well a mind-body connection outside the usual focus on day-to-day stress and emotional distress is relevant. And published studies provide support for this understanding in relation to conditions such as chronic fatigue syndrome, inflammatory bowel disease, autoimmune diseases, migraine, asthma, fibromyalgia, and others whose cause we still don't fully understand, and whose treatment remains challenging. And the corollary question that needs to be asked and addressed is whether this understanding offers new pathways for medical healing.

Though at first I wasn't looking for it, the specter of repressed emotions arose repeatedly. Ironically, the mind-body connection was often relevant in patients who did not complain of emotional distress and who, if anything, would argue against the existence of such a link.

In the coming chapters, I will present intriguing observations that suggested that the burden of repressed emotions plays an unrecognized and unsuspected role in patients with commonly encountered medical disorders whose cause and treatment remain an enigma. I hope these patients' stories will ring true for readers. I will also discuss published evidence that supports this new understanding.

I'm not suggesting that this understanding pertains to every patient with these disorders. I believe it is relevant in a proportion of patients that differs from condition to condition. Genetic predisposition clearly plays a major role, as do physical or environmental triggers that we don't fully understand. Research has taught us a lot about the pathophysiology of those conditions, although too often we still don't know what triggers initiate the culprit pathophysiologic processes.

With regard to many of those conditions, I cannot offer a reliable estimate as to the proportion of patients in whom the burden of repressed emotions plays a role. But based on my clinical experience and data from published studies, I suspect that a link to repressed emotions could be relevant in half or more of patients with conditions such as chronic fatigue syndrome (Ch. 12), fibromyalgia and other unexplained chronic pain syndromes (Ch. 13), and in patients with unexplained anxiety (Ch. 15). I suspect it is relevant in a significant but lower proportion of patients with migraine (Ch. 13), inflammatory bowel disease (Ch. 11), autoimmune diseases (Ch. 14), and possibly other conditions not discussed in this book, such as non-allergic asthma, unexpected postpartum depression, and others.

Given the persisting puzzle of the origin of so many disorders, the limitations and adverse effects of current treatment, the need in many disorders for lifelong treatment, and the continued suffering of many patients for years, and even decades, we must begin to consider the unexamined role of our most powerful emotions, a role that has never been explored because those emotions are not consciously experienced and are not reported.

Chapter 11

The Mystery of Inflammatory Bowel Disease

T*wo common conditions* that affect intestinal function and cause symptoms that include abdominal pain and diarrhea are irritable bowel syndrome (IBS) and inflammatory bowel disease (IBD). IBS is considered a "functional" disease in that there are no pathological changes, such as inflammation in the bowel wall. IBD, which affects about 1.5 million people in the U.S. and 2.2 million in Europe, differs in that it is characterized by pathological changes caused by inflammation in the intestinal wall that can lead to serious complications including abscesses, intestinal obstruction, and others.

The most common forms of IBD are Crohn's disease and ulcerative colitis. Numerous studies have investigated their possible cause, but no causative infectious agent has been identified. The role of changes in the bacterial population of the gut is being studied. At present, ulcerative colitis and Crohn's disease are considered autoimmune diseases, meaning the inflammation is caused by the body's immune reaction against itself. Despite decades of research, however, the cause that triggers this autoimmune reaction remains unknown.

———————————————————————————————————

John, 56, had a tough countenance; he was a no-nonsense guy. He had suffered from severe Crohn's disease and its complications for decades, and had endured many surgical procedures. He was referred to me for hypertension that had never been well-controlled and had become increasingly severe.

During John's initial visit, when I asked him about his family medical history, he told me his father had died at a young age, 42. I, of course, asked the cause: sudden cardiac death.

As discussed above, when a patient reports that a parent died at a young age, physicians always ask the cause, but we are not taught to ask, "How old were you when your parent died, and how did it affect you?" The death, and particularly the sudden death, of a parent during our childhood is usually a major trauma.

"How old were you when your father died?"

"Seventeen."

"Did you grieve?"

"No. I'm tough."

"Oh. By the way, how old were you when the colitis started?"

"Seventeen."

The coincidence was striking. Equally striking was the absence of grief. When I asked John if he thought there might be a connection between his father's sudden death and the onset at that time of his colitis, I was surprised that he saw no possible connection. He had experienced no deep pain, so he never thought the two were related. Ironically, my suspicion that the colitis was linked to the trauma arose not **despite** the absence of painful grief: It arose **because** of its absence.

I began to pay more attention to the recent and childhood history of patients I was seeing who had IBD, and to the presence, absence, and severity of emotional distress they were experiencing. Again, I want to emphasize that I do not believe that IBD is linked to repressed emotions in most patients. Genetic predisposition and other factors, known and unknown, are the driving force in many. However, I suspect that, in many, repressed emotions can silently play a role, either as a cause or a contributor. As I will discuss, reported research also suggests such a link.

Renee, 79, came to see me for routine hypertension that was detected when she was 74. She was retired. Her husband had died nine years earlier. She had no symptoms of anxiety or depression and regarded herself as an optimist.

But what interested me more was an interesting story that was unrelated to her hypertension. When I reviewed her medical history, she mentioned that she had had ulcerative colitis that was diagnosed when she was just eight. It was not mild. She had frequent diarrhea and episodes of bleeding that required hospitalizations.

Her history was unusual in that after suffering from colitis for 20 years, it suddenly and permanently ceased when she was 28. And there was a story regarding that unexpected outcome.

Renee's mother, a perfectionist, had criticized Renee during the entirety of her childhood. Everything Renee did was wrong.

Later on, when Renee was married and in her 20s, her mother traveled to visit her every few months, staying with Renee for several days. She remained her old, critical self. When Renee was 28, her husband pointed out something she'd never noticed: whenever her mother visited, Renee had to run to the bathroom much more frequently.

Renee listened, then did something she had never done before: She told her mother bluntly that if she didn't stop criticizing her, her mother would never again be allowed in her house.

Two things happened: Renee's mother stopped criticizing her. And with no other intervention, Renee's colitis of 20 years resolved, quickly and completely!

I was fascinated by Renee's story. There was no question in her mind that the cessation of her colitis was related to her recognition of the lifelong emotional abuse she'd endured from an early age, and to her standing up to her mother for the first time, feeling and conveying her anger, and demanding an end to what had been so hard to bear.

As intolerable as the abusive constant criticism was to her as an adult, it could only have been much worse for a child, who didn't recognize that it was abuse that was far out of the norm, and that it was not her fault. And as a child, Renee had been helpless to stop her mother.

Ulcerative colitis is generally not a condition that suddenly stops. There are periods when it is less active than others, but it rarely suddenly ceases completely. Renee's story strongly suggested, in retrospect, that the years-long unchallenged

emotional abuse could have caused her colitis. Becoming aware
of the anger, and, as an adult twenty years later, defending
that child, with no other intervention, brought a sudden end
to two decades of colitis.

The relationship between psychological factors and IBD and IBS is complex and remains inadequately understood. A key area of confusion is the bidirectionality of the mind-body connection: Emotional stress, such as depression and anxiety, could be a causative factor in the development of IBD, or conversely, could be a consequence of years of suffering from IBD. Also confusing is that although studies inform us that patients suffering from emotional distress tend to report more IBD symptoms, they do not confirm a relationship between emotional distress and objective evidence of inflammation.[1]

One area in which studies report consistent findings concerns the association between IBD and adverse childhood experiences. Consistent with my observations, studies have strongly documented an association of IBD and IBS with childhood abuse or trauma.[2-6] A review of studies found a history of childhood physical or sexual abuse in about 50 percent of patients with IBD or IBS.[7] Several studies reported an increased prevalence of childhood sexual abuse among patients with IBS.[4,8,9] And the severity of symptoms in patients with IBS was also found to be greater in patients with a history of abuse.[4]

However, the role of repression in coping with adverse childhood events, and its relevance to the development and treatment of IBD and IBS have not been studied. It is an aspect of the mind-body connection that neither patients nor physicians are aware of. In one report, IBS was found to be associated with "alexithymia," a condition characterized by the absence of use of words for feelings that bears similarity to a repressive coping style.[10] However, overall, research psychologists have overlooked the role of repressed emotions.

Many studies have looked at the effect of antidepressants in patients with IBD, and recent reviews of studies confirm a beneficial effect with regard to IBD.[11,12] One study reported improvement in 59 percent of patients treated with a tricyclic antidepressant.[13] Another reported a reduction in the need for intensification of treatment for IBD among patients treated with an antidepressant.[14] Antidepressants have also been shown to be effective in patients with IBS.[15] An antidepressant can also help reduce the emotional distress that is a result of chronic illness, independent of its effect, or lack of effect, on the disease itself.

I suspect that studies of the efficacy of antidepressants in IBD included mainly patients who were depressed or anxious, and thus were willing to participate in such a trial. I also suspect that patients without emotional distress—often including sur-vivors of abuse or trauma who avoided emotional consequences by virtue of repression, and in whom a mind-body connection is, therefore, unlikely to be considered—are less likely to be offered an antidepressant, and less likely to participate in studies of antidepressants.

Thus, the potential efficacy of antidepressants in treating IBD is unlikely to have been assessed in patients who have repressed powerful emotions related to adverse events such as childhood abuse or trauma and who don't suffer from anxiety or depression. The benefit of treating these patients with an antidepressant should be considered and studied, especially among patients who respond poorly to IBD treatment or suffer from treatment side effects, given the chronicity of IBD and the relative safety of antidepressants.

There is, of course, another question: Can gaining awareness of repressed emotions ameliorate IBD? Renee's story suggests that it can, but clearly that question has not yet been examined or considered.

Recent research in IBD has also looked at the role of the autonomic nervous system, which consists of two limbs: the **sympathetic nervous system (SNS)** and the **parasympathetic (vagal) system**. The SNS mediates our fight or flight reflexes. It is stimulated by physical and emotional stress, with effects often mediated by the hormone adrenaline. Activity of the **parasympathetic** limb is conveyed mainly through the vagus nerve. It is frequently referred to as **vagal tone**. It serves to innervate functions such as digestion.

These two limbs, the sympathetic and the parasympathetic (vagal), bear a reciprocal relationship to each other; stimulation of sympathetic tone inhibits parasympathetic (vagal) tone. Thus, when our sympathetic tone is high, as in stressful situations, our parasympathetic tone is low.

Studies inform us that sympathetic tone is increased and parasympathetic (vagal) tone is reduced in patients with IBS and IBD.[2,16-18] They also inform us that a reduced vagal tone is associated with increased gut symptoms and increased inflammation, as documented by increased levels of pro-inflammatory mediators such as TNF-alpha.[2,17]

Two findings further suggest the involvement of increased sympathetic tone and decreased parasympathetic tone in the pathogenesis of IBD. One is the fascinating finding that interventions that increase vagal tone, such as vagal nerve stimulation, can reduce the release of TNF-alpha and ameliorate symptoms and disease activity in IBD patients.[17] The other is that medication that reduces sympathetic tone, such as the antihypertensive drug clonidine, is associated with improvement in IBD symptoms and in the disease course.[19] However, clonidine has side effects that discourage its widespread use in treating chronic IBD.

These findings in IBD patients could very well be linked to emotions, as emotions routinely increase SNS tone and reduce parasympathetic (vagal) tone. Emotions related to severe adverse childhood events could play a role in IBD patients, including—perhaps particularly—the powerful emotions that were of necessity repressed but persist beneath conscious awareness. They do so even in, and, perhaps especially in, survivors who are not experiencing overt emotional consequences such as anxiety or depression.

Finally, I want to emphasize again that in many patients IBD is not driven by a mind-body link. However, I believe we need to further examine the role of repressed emotions as a causative or exacerbating factor in some. More important, we need to examine whether this understanding can provide new directions in treatment.

References

1. Sexton KA, Walker JR, Graff LA, et al. Evidence of Bidirectional Associations Between Perceived Stress and Symptom Activity: A Prospective Longitudinal Investigation in Inflammatory Bowel Disease. Inflammatory Bowel Dis. 2017 Mar;23(3):473-483. doi: 10.1097/ MIB.0000000000001040. PMID: 28221251.

2. Kolacz J, Kovacic KK, Porges SW. Traumatic stress and the autonomic brain-gut connection in development: Polyvagal Theory as an integrative framework for psychosocial and gastrointestinal pathology. Dev Psychobiol. 2019 Jul;61(5):796-809. doi: 10.1002/dev.21852. Epub 2019 Apr 5. PMID: 30953358.

3. Afari N, Ahumada SM, Wright LJ, et al. Psychological trauma and functional somatic syndromes: a systematic review and meta-analysis. Psychosom Med. 2014 Jan;76(1):2-11. doi: 10.1097/PSY.0000000000000010. Epub 2013 Dec 12. PMID: 24336429; PMCID: PMC3894419.

4. Longstreth GF, Wolde-Tsadik G. Irritable bowel-type symptoms in HMO examinees. Prevalence, demographics, and clinical correlates. Dig Dis Sci. 1993 Sep;38(9):1581-9. doi: 10.1007/BF01303163. PMID: 8359067.

5. Drossman DA, Leserman J, Nachman G, Li ZM, Gluck H, Toomey TC, Mitchell CM. Sexual and physical abuse in women with functional or organic gastrointestinal disorders. Ann Intern Med. 1990 Dec 1;113(11):828-33. doi: 10.7326/0003-4819-113-11-828. PMID: 2240898.

6. Goodwin RD, Hoven CW, Murison R, Hotopf M. Association between childhood physical abuse and gastrointestinal disorders and migraine in adulthood. Am J Public Health. 2003 Jul;93(7):1065-7. doi: 10.2105/ajph.93.7.1065. PMID: 12835180; PMCID: PMC1447904.

7. Drossman DA, Talley NJ, Leserman J, Olden KW, Barreiro MA. Sexual and physical abuse and gastrointestinal illness. Review and recommendations. Ann Intern Med. 1995 Nov 15;123(10):782-94. doi: 10.7326/0003-4819-123-10-199511150-00007. PMID: 7574197.

8. Ross CA. Childhood sexual abuse and psychosomatic symptoms in irritable bowel syndrome. J Child Sex Abus. 2005;14(1):27-38. doi: 10.1300/J070v14n01_02. PMID: 15914403.

9. Paras ML, Murad MH, Chen LP, et al. Sexual abuse and lifetime diagnosis of somatic disorders: a systematic review and meta-analysis. JAMA. 2009 Aug 5;302(5):550-61. doi: 10.1001/jama.2009.1091. PMID: 19654389.

10. Phillips K, Wright BJ, Kent S. Psychosocial predictors of irritable bowel syndrome diagnosis and symptom severity. J Psychosom Res. 2013 Nov;75(5):467-74. doi: 10.1016/j.jpsychores.2013.08.002. Epub 2013 Aug 9. PMID: 24182637.

11. Macer BJD, Prady SL, Mikocka-Walus A. Antidepressants in Inflammatory Bowel Disease: A Systematic Review. Inflamm Bowel Dis. 2017 Apr;23(4):534-550. doi: 10.1097/MIB.0000000000001059. PMID: 28267046.

12. Drossman DA. Treatment of residual inflammatory bowel disease symptoms with low-dose tricyclic antidepressants: why not? J Clin Gastroenterol. 2014 May-Jun;48(5):390-2. doi: 10.1097/MCG.0000000000000098. PMID: 24714103.

13. Iskandar HN, Cassell B, Kanuri N, et al. Tricyclic antidepressants for management of residual symptoms in inflammatory bowel disease. J Clin Gastroenterol. 2014 May-Jun;48(5):423-9. doi: 10.1097/MCG.0000000000000049. PMID: 24406434; PMCID: PMC4111227.

14. Kristensen MS, Kjærulff TM, Ersbøll AK, Green A, Hallas J, Thygesen LC. The Influence of Antidepressants on the Disease Course Among Patients With Crohn's Disease and Ulcerative Colitis-A Danish Nationwide Register-Based Cohort Study. Inflamm Bowel Dis. 2019 Apr 11;25(5):886-893. doi: 10.1093/ibd/izy367. Erratum in: Inflamm Bowel Dis. 2019 Oct 18;25(11):e152. PMID: 30551218; PMCID: PMC6458526.

15. Ford AC, Talley NJ, Schoenfeld PS, Quigley EM, Moayyedi P. Efficacy of antidepressants and psychological therapies in irritable bowel syndrome: systematic review and meta-analysis. Gut. 2009 Mar;58(3):367-78. doi: 10.1136/gut.2008.163162. Epub 2008 Nov 10. PMID: 19001059.

16. Maule S, Pierangeli G, et al. Sympathetic hyperactivity in patients with ulcerative colitis. Clin Auton Res. 2007 Aug;17(4):217-20. doi: 10.1007/s10286-007-0425-0. Epub 2007 Jun 15. PMID: 17574503.

17. Bonaz B, Sinniger V, Pellissier S. Therapeutic Potential of Vagus Nerve Stimulation for Inflammatory Bowel Diseases. Front Neurosci. 2021

Mar 22;15:650971. doi: 10.3389/fnins.2021.650971. PMID: 33828455; PMCID: PMC8019822.

18. Kim KN, Yao Y, Ju SY. Heart rate variability and inflammatory bowel disease in humans: A systematic review and meta-analysis. Medicine (Baltimore). 2020 Nov 25;99(48):e23430. doi: 10.1097/MD.0000000000023430. PMID: 33235125; PMCID: PMC7710256.

19. Furlan R., Ardizzone S., Palazzolo L., et al. Sympathetic overactivity in active ulcerative colitis: Effects of clonidine. Am. J. Physiol. Regul. Integr. Comp. Physiol. 2006;290(1):R224-R232. doi:10.1152/ajpregu.00442.2005. Epub 2005 Aug 25. PMID: 16123227.

Chapter 12

Chronic Fatigue Syndrome

Chronic fatigue syndrome (CFS), now known scientifically as myalgic encephalitis/chronic fatigue syndrome (ME/CFS), was identified over sixty years ago. Unfortunately, CFS affects the energy and quality of life of two million Americans, often severely. Patients are mostly young or middle-aged.

Patients typically experience fatigue, sleep difficulties, muscle aches, difficulty concentrating, and other symptoms. Typically, the onset of symptoms is sudden.

Physicians regularly search for a cause. A chronic viral infection is usually suspected. In the past, the suspected infection was "chronic mono," the mononucleosis virus. More recently, suspicion has focused on chronic Lyme disease. However, infectious disease experts have concluded that CFS usually is *not* caused by infection or its aftermath. Despite a considerable amount of research, its cause remains a frustrating, unsolved mystery with no clear direction to pursue. To this day, in most cases, physicians are unable to identify a cause, and it is difficult to find effective treatment. Symptoms can persist for years or decades, wrecking the lives of many.

There are no tests that can diagnose CFS or provide clues to its cause. In fact, one of the diagnostic criteria of CFS is that all lab results are normal, with assessment for inflammation, autoimmunity, endocrine dysfunction, or gluten sensitivity.[1]

Every few years a new cause and treatment are suggested, but end up leading to a dead end. There is no pharmacologic treatment documented to be effective. The most recent drug therapy tested was a monoclonal antibody, rituximab. Here, too, a well-controlled trial demonstrated unequivocally that there was no benefit.[2] In some cases, an antidepressant can be helpful, although it is unclear whether depression is a cause or consequence of CFS.[3,4]

After decades of research concerning CFS, we don't know its cause, there are no abnormal diagnostic tests, and there is no treatment proven reliably effective. There is a desperate need for better understanding and treatment. In this context, it is imperative to consider the unstudied role of repressed emotions in its genesis.

Hank, 53, had suffered from CFS for ten years, and it was getting worse. Although he managed to work regular hours as an accountant, he had no residual energy and spent the rest of his time in bed.

I asked about psychological factors. Yes, he had job stress, but who doesn't? He said he was not depressed. He was unmarried, and homosexual.

I inquired about his history and childhood. He was surprised. No physician had ever asked about his past. He had grown up in rural Pennsylvania. His mother was an alcoholic and his father was physically abusive.

I asked what it was like growing up, knowing he was homosexual in a rural area in those days. He said it had been rough. He didn't fit in. His father rejected him. He described school as years of torture.

I asked again if he suffered from depression. He again said no. "That wouldn't serve any purpose."

Again, I was hearing a combination of a severely painful childhood and the absence of acknowledged emotional consequences in a patient with an otherwise unexplained medical condition, CFS. Over the years I have observed this pattern in most of the patients I've seen who had CFS. I also suspect that clinical psychologists are less likely to see patients with this pattern, again because of the absence of symptoms of anxiety or depression.

Again, the question arises: Could this understanding lead to any meaningful approach to treatment?

Peter, 22, had seen several doctors in his hometown in Massachusetts for two unexplained problems that had started when he was 18: high blood pressure and CFS.

His fatigue began in his freshman year in college and worsened year by year. He had done well in college and started law school, but due to increasing fatigue, he had dropped out in the middle of his first semester.

Peter was thin and had no extraordinary family history of hypertension. Frankly, at 22, someone like Peter should not have hypertension. Yet at his first visit, despite being on two medications, his blood pressure was quite high, 160/90. It was not "white coat" hypertension; his blood pressure was equally high at home.

He brought with him files of blood test results that revealed no explanation for either the hypertension or the CFS. I didn't need to order any tests; any necessary ones had already been performed.

With Peter having two unexplained chronic medical conditions, I considered the possibility of a mind-body connection. I asked about his life, current and past. He insisted he was neither depressed nor anxious; his only concerns were his unexplained fatigue and hypertension.

I found it surprising that during four years of unexplained hypertension and fatigue no doctor had considered a mind-body connection. But I could understand why, as Peter didn't seem emotionally troubled. And repressed emotions are on the radar of few physicians. Once again, my experience was teaching me the important point that, almost paradoxically, among patients with unexplained medical disorders, it is often the patient who appears the least anxious or depressed in whom a mind-body cause can be operative yet unlikely to be considered.

I tackled Peter's hypertension first because that was his reason for seeing me. He was taking two medications that target the kidneys, an angiotensin-receptor antagonist (ARB) and a diuretic, which had had no effect, suggesting that his hypertension likely was not driven by the kidneys, and was instead driven by the sympathetic nervous system (SNS), whose stimulation is usually attributable to emotion. His rapid heart rate, 96 beats per minute, also pointed to the SNS. Peter claimed he was not anxious, but his heart rate was behaving as if he was. He was unaware of anxiety even though it was physiologically conspicuously evident. I asked more questions.

Peter's parents were divorced. Their marriage, during his childhood, had been extremely troubled, with frequent shouting, altercations, and bitterness that created a persistently toxic environment in which to grow up. Peter said that throughout, he had been okay; he had not felt distressed. But his unexplained hypertension, rapid heart rate, and fatigue strongly suggested that, unknown to him, beneath that calmness lay an emotional storm.

I told Peter that the continual turmoil he had described sounded dreadful. I conveyed that I was amazed at how he had come through it so well, and wondered if that burden of emotion, though unfelt, might underlie both his unexplained hypertension and his unexplained chronic fatigue. I said there might be a possibility of healing.

Peter understood. He asked what the next step might be. I suggested first that I would replace his two antihypertensive medications with a beta-blocker and alpha-blocker to target the SNS. Second, given the relentless upheaval in his childhood, I suggested the option of psychotherapy. I asked him to reflect on our discussion and to come back in a week.

A week later, his blood pressure had normalized on the new medication, further implicating the SNS and emotions in the genesis of his hypertension. However, he said his fatigue was worse, and he was now feeling extremely anxious; he could not function. He said he had an appointment to see a psychologist.

He asked if I could prescribe anything for the severe anxiety that was now clearly overwhelming him. His anxiety, his request for medication, and his willingness to see a psychologist indicated that powerful emotions, unfelt for years, were now much closer to the surface.

He readily agreed to take an antidepressant. I also prescribed a small supply of alprazolam, an anti-anxiety drug, that he could take during the 10 to 14 days before the antidepressant would take effect.

I saw Peter two weeks later. His blood pressure was 130/70, his heart rate, slowed by the beta-blocker, was 70, and he was feeling much better. His energy had improved considerably, and his fatigue was already less than it had been in four years. He remained on the medication and returned to law school.

Peter's dramatic response to the antidepressant, and the normal results of every test, strongly suggested that his chronic fatigue had a mind-body origin despite the absence of symptoms such as depression or anxiety during those four years. There might be an opportunity for him to do the work of emotional healing, but it was unclear when. Peter would now be fortified by the perspective of an adult and the knowledge that the child within survived those challenges. Even so, facing those emotions now could still be difficult. That is why choosing this path must be the patient's decision, and cannot be coerced.

Peter's story illustrates some of the obstacles to emotional healing. Given the years of turmoil at a sensitive age, powerful emotions were repressed for good reason. Also, in the absence of conscious awareness of distressful emotions, most trauma survivors are resistant to the idea that they are harboring such emotions.

Peter's response to the antidepressant, although a blessing, could lessen his motivation to seek a healing awareness. And, with or without therapy, those emotions might be less accessible while taking the antidepressant, as the purpose of an antidepressant is to reduce accessibility to troubling emotions.

The question remains as to whether and when Peter might reduce the dose of the antidepressant and seek a healing pathway. In the meantime, for the first time in years, he was feeling and functioning much better.

Consistent with these observations, studies examining the possible mind-body connection of CFS have documented a strong relationship between childhood abuse or trauma and the future development of CFS.[5-7] In a meta-analysis of studies, Afari reported a strong association of CFS with trauma during childhood or adulthood.[8] Also supporting a mind-body origin are studies that report that SNS tone is increased in patients with CFS.[9]

Studies reveal an increased likelihood of developing CFS among trauma survivors suffering from depression, anxiety, or PTSD. However, my observations strongly suggest that CFS can also be linked to a history of childhood trauma, abuse, or severe family dysfunction even in the absence of overt psychological sequelae.

In this situation, physicians are unlikely to consider a mind-body origin or a trial of an antidepressant.

Although Peter's CFS responded dramatically to an antidepressant, the results of studies of treatment with any medication are mostly inconclusive. To date, studies have not reported a substantial benefit of antidepressants, although there is a paucity of reliable studies.[10] In a controlled trial, the antidepressant fluoxetine was found to be ineffective.[11] However, an anti-depressant was found to be effective in a more recent study that observed the response over a longer period of time.[12] I also suspect that patients with a history of trauma, abuse, or emotional upheaval who don't suffer from emotional distress by virtue of repression are less likely to be offered treatment with an antidepressant, and less likely to have participated in studies of treatment with an antidepressant. At this time, given the prolonged course of CFS, its unknown origin, and the absence of any treatment known to be reliably effective, I believe a trial of an antidepressant merits consideration, even in, and perhaps particularly in, patients who are not depressed.

I don't believe a burden of repressed emotions is the cause of CFS in all patients. But my experience suggests that repressed emotions play an unseen role in many patients with this disorder. Given the futility of decades of research in understanding and treating CFS, I believe this understanding, linking CFS to powerful repressed emotions, merits greater consideration.

References

1. Bansal AS. Investigating unexplained fatigue in general practice with a particular focus on CFS/ME. BMC Fam Pract. 2016 Jul 19;17:81.

doi: 10.1186/s12875-016-0493-0. PMID: 27436349; PMCID: PMC4950776.

2. Fluge Ø, Rekeland IG, Lien K, et al. B-Lymphocyte Depletion in Patients With Myalgic Encephalomyelitis/Chronic Fatigue Syndrome: A Randomized, Double-Blind, Placebo-Controlled Trial. Ann Intern Med. 2019 May 7;170(9):585-593. doi: 10.7326/M18-1451. Epub 2019 Apr 2. PMID: 30934066.

3. Taerk GS, Toner BB, Salit IE, Garfinkel PE, Ozersky S. Depression in patients with neuromyasthenia (benign myalgic encephalomyelitis). Int J Psychiatry Med. 1987;17(1):49-56. doi: 10.2190/8r67-n9er-xr74-9ra7. PMID: 3583562.

4. Van Houdenhove B, Pae CU, Luyten P. Chronic fatigue syndrome: is there a role for non-antidepressant pharmacotherapy? Expert Opin Pharmacother. 2010 Feb;11(2):215-23. doi: 10.1517/14656560903487744. PMID: 20088743.

5. Kempke S, Luyten P, Claes S, Van Wambeke P, Bekaert P, Goossens L, Van Houdenhove B. The prevalence and impact of early childhood trauma in Chronic Fatigue Syndrome. J Psychiatr Res. 2013 May;47(5):664-9. doi: 10.1016/j.jpsychires.2013.01.021. Epub 2013 Feb 16. PMID: 23421962.

6. Heim C, Wagner D, Maloney E, et al. Early adverse experience and risk for chronic fatigue syndrome: results from a population-based study. Arch Gen Psychiatry. 2006 Nov;63(11):1258-66. doi: 10.1001/archpsyc.63.11.1258. PMID: 17088506.

7. Romans S, Belaise C, Martin J, Morris E, Raffi A. Childhood abuse and later medical disorders in women. An epidemiological study. Psychother Psychosom. 2002 May-Jun;71(3):141-50. doi: 10.1159/000056281. PMID: 12021556.

8. Afari N, Ahumada SM, Wright LJ, et al. Psychological trauma and functional somatic syndromes: a systematic review and meta-analysis. Psychosom Med. 2014 Jan;76(1):2-11. doi: 10.1097/PSY.0000000000000010. Epub 2013 Dec 12. PMID: 24336429; PMCID: PMC3894419.

9. Meeus M, Goubert D, De Backer F, et al. Heart rate variability in patients with fibromyalgia and patients with chronic fatigue syndrome: a

systematic review. Semin Arthritis Rheum. 2013 Oct;43(2):279-87. doi: 10.1016/j.semarthrit.2013.03.004. Epub 2013 Jul 6. PMID: 23838093.

10. Richman S, Morris MC, Broderick G, Craddock TJA, Klimas NG, Fletcher MA. Pharmaceutical Interventions in Chronic Fatigue Syndrome: A Literature-based Commentary. Clin Ther. 2019 May;41(5):798-805. doi: 10.1016/j.clinthera.2019.02.011. Epub 2019 Mar 11. PMID: 30871727; PMCID: PMC6543846.

11. Vercoulen JH, Swanink CM, Zitman FG, et al. Randomised, double-blind, placebo-controlled study of fluoxetine in chronic fatigue syndrome. Lancet. 1996 Mar 30;347(9005):858-61. doi: 10.1016/s0140-6736(96)91345-8. PMID: 8622391.

12. Thomas MA, Smith AP. An investigation of the long-term benefits of antidepressant medication in the recovery of patients with chronic fatigue syndrome. Hum Psychopharmacol. 2006 Dec;21(8):503-9. doi: 10.1002/hup.805. PMID: 16981220.

Chapter 13

Repression and Chronic Pain Disorders
Back Pain, Migraine, and Fibromyalgia Syndrome (FMS)

There are several conditions dominated by chronic pain where, remarkably, after decades of research we don't know their cause, laboratory testing consistently lacks any abnormality, there is no cure, and the results of treatment are often disappointing. A few examples are back pain, migraine, and fibromyalgia syndrome (FMS).

Back Pain
The Work of Dr. John Sarno

Dr. John Sarno was a pioneer in linking medically unexplained pain syndromes, particularly back pain, to repressed emotions, an understanding that has dramatically helped many patients. Dr. Sarno authored several books, including his first, a widely known bestseller, *Healing Back Pain*. He witnessed the rapid, dramatic improvement that can occur after patients gain awareness of emotions they had avoided.

I was fortunate to know Dr. Sarno. I enjoyed our conversations and contributed a chapter to his book, *The Divided Mind*. However, I believe there are both similarities and differences between the patients with back pain Dr. Sarno encountered and the patients with hypertension and other medical disorders I encounter.

It is often difficult to differentiate those in whom back pain has a mind-body origin from those in whom there is an orthopedic cause. Radiologic abnormalities are extremely common among those with, and even those without, back pain and it can be difficult to discern whether it is causally related to the back pain or is merely an incidental finding.

In contrast, in dealing with patients with hypertension, it is clear to me that among those with a typical presentation of hypertension, the condition usually is *not* a mind-body disorder. It is attributable to genetics and health habits—not emotions. As discussed above, it is in patients with atypical forms of hypertension in whom hypertension is most likely to be linked to repressed emotions.

Another difference lies in the description by Dr. Sarno of the "symptom imperative," meaning that the symptom, the back pain, serves the purpose of deflecting attention away from emotions related to stress. Patients with hypertension usually have no symptoms; hence the term "the silent killer." Hypertension does not serve a purpose of deflecting attention.

Another difference is that Dr. Sarno's patients with mind-body-related back pain had symptoms (pain) but no identifiable underlying medical cause or pathology. My findings pertain to a broader range of patients. Some similarly have unexplained pain or other symptoms with no identifiable pathology (e.g., chronic fatigue syndrome, migraine, fibromyalgia). Others, though, have blatant physiologic abnormalities, such as hypertension or asthma, and some have medical conditions that are clearly associated with pathological changes, such as inflammatory bowel disease or autoimmune conditions.

Another important difference is that many patients saw Dr. Sarno after reading one of his books and were already open to the possibility that their back pain had a mind-body origin. Many were somewhat aware that there were stressful issues in their current life that they were avoiding dealing with. In contrast, most of my patients come to me for my medical expertise. They do not come seeking to explore a mind-body connection, and my suggestion of such a connection usually comes as a surprise. I encounter resistance to that explanation in many.

Also, Dr. Sarno's experience often involves physical symptoms linked to the avoidance by patients of emotions related to current stressful situations. In contrast, I encounter patients who have deeply repressed emotions that are more often related to events that occurred years or decades earlier, often from childhood. And in most, the repression was necessary for emotional survival and was at the heart of their resilience. That is why, in many, the emotions understandably remain difficult to access.

Finally, I believe a key difference lies in our perspective on repression. Dr. Sarno's focus was on the deleterious impact of repression, and on treatment aimed at overcoming the repression. While I similarly view repression as linked to medical consequences, I cannot emphasize enough that in many patients I don't view repression as pathological. Yes, it is interfering with health and well-being, but in many repression had been a defense that at one time was necessary for psychological survival—a defense we need to consider addressing, but must first acknowledge, and honor.

In summary, I believe that there are similarities and differences in the phenomena Dr. Sarno and I are describing. We both, however, have described patients who were affected by emotions they were unaware of. And we both recognize that, in some patients, awareness is possible and can lead to healing. And in some it can occur rapidly.

Migraine

Many people suffer from migraine headaches. The prevalence of migraine has been reported to be approximately 18 percent in women and 6 percent in men.[1,2]

Migraine headaches can last for up to two or three days and can recur regularly for years. They are not dangerous but, for many, they considerably impair quality of life. Treatment for migraine has improved, but leaves a lot to be desired in terms of effectiveness and side effects. Thus, the need for new ideas and new approaches to treatment remains.

Several factors suggest that, for many, migraine is a mind-body disorder. Migraine is more likely to be seen among those with psychiatric disorders including depression, generalized anxiety disorder, panic disorder, PTSD, and bipolar disorder.[3,4] Here again, many studies have reported an increased risk of migraine among adults with a history of adverse childhood experiences such as abuse or trauma.[5-10] Among patients with migraine who report a history of childhood abuse, the onset of migraine headaches occurs at a younger age.[11] Migraine is also associated with an increased incidence of disorders including fibromyalgia and chronic fatigue syndrome that are also associated with childhood abuse or trauma.[9] The association of migraine with childhood events also extends to more commonly encountered events that are less likely to be considered trauma yet have substantial impact, such as long-lasting financial difficulties in the family, a family member having been seriously or chronically ill, serious family conflicts, and parental divorce.[12] Also, in patients with migraine who report adverse childhood experiences, an increase in inflammatory factors (high-sensitivity C-reactive protein, interleukin-6, and tissue necrosis factor-alpha) has been reported.[13]

Having encountered many patients who suffer from recurrent migraine, I usually ask carefully about their psychosocial history. In accord with the studies, a seemingly high proportion of patients have reported a history of abuse, trauma, or periods of overwhelming stress. But I've also noticed something that, again, is not discussed or looked at in studies: Many patients reported having suffered no lingering psychological consequences.

I wondered whether their migraine headaches might be related to their history of having coped successfully and avoided emotional consequences by virtue of repression. Virtually no studies have examined or considered the possible link between repressed emotions and migraine headaches. In this context, Carol's story grabbed my attention.

Carol, 48, was slim and had never had hypertension. However, during the previous few months, she had been experiencing fluctuating blood pressure elevation and was feeling anxious. Her blood pressure, which had spiked as high as 176/99, sometimes remained elevated for a week or two, then settled down, only to increase again. She was otherwise well except for a history of migraine headaches since her teen years. Her headaches occurred monthly, coinciding with her menstrual cycle and lasting for about three days.

Carol's physician wanted to start her on hypertension medication, but Carol didn't like the idea of taking lifelong medication. She still wanted to know the cause; the sudden onset of her hypertension made no sense to her.

There did not seem to be a medical reason for it. Although she had a family history of hypertension, she was not overweight and had previously had perfectly normal blood pressure readings. Tests to screen for an uncommon cause had yielded normal results.

The fluctuation in Carol's blood pressure strongly suggested that her blood pressure elevation was attributable to stimulation of the sympathetic nervous system (SNS) rather than to the usual origin of hypertension related to the kidneys. With the link between the SNS and emotions, I explored possible emotional factors.

Carol was a delightful woman. She laughed easily and had no prior history of anxiety or depression.

Carol was accompanied by her husband. They were happily married, with two teenage children who were well. She had met her husband when they were 15-year-old classmates. They struck me as one of those couples that were meant to be together. She worked in the real estate industry; work was not particularly stressful.

Clearly, current stress was not a major problem.

In obtaining the family medical history, Carol told me that her father had died a few months before her first visit with me. He was in his early 80s and had had a long-standing heart condition. Her blood pressure elevation appeared a few weeks before he died. Carol wondered if it was related to that event. I didn't think the expected death of a parent in his 80s would cause hypertension, especially in someone whose life was otherwise in such good order. But the timing was interesting. I wondered if there was more to the story; there was.

I asked Carol about her relationship with her father during her childhood. She said she'd had a love/hate relationship with him. She related a painful childhood story. When she was 12, her father had an extra-marital affair. Her mother left home and stayed away for six months. She came back, but from then on remained angry.

Both parents drank heavily. Carol's father was very critical and emotionally abusive. Her siblings suffered emotionally. Carol, though, had managed well, not coincidentally because of the emotional support, beginning a few years later at 15, from her boyfriend/husband-to-be.

Carol's story was another example of a patient surviving emotionally despite an emotionally troubling childhood. She never suffered from depression or anxiety, was a good wife and mom, and was a delightfully cheerful person.

Yes, there was a temporal link between her new hypertension and her father's death, but it seemed unlikely that his death, by itself, could be the cause of her persisting hypertension and anxiety. I suggested the possible relevance of the emotional distress that had surrounded her in childhood. I discussed how the gift of repression and of emotional connectedness and support had helped her move on relatively unscarred. I emphasized the resilience of that young girl.

The situation suggested that her father's death had triggered painful, long-repressed emotions. I suggested that the emotions she now felt were ones that had fortunately been repressed when they could have overwhelmed her. And that the emotional pain she was experiencing now, rather than representing an emotional disorder, offered an opportunity to experience and finally confront those locked-up emotions and heal—now, when her life was stable, and when she had the loving support of her husband. And with the knowledge now that she had successfully survived those awful years.

Carol immediately understood. She began to cry. She was not distressed by her crying. She understood the opportunity for healing, the opportunity to comfort the young girl within who had managed so well by not feeling.

On her return visit, Carol related that she was feeling well, was experiencing some of the walled-off emotions, and felt she was healing. Her blood pressure, on no medication, was normal.

Over the next several months, she noticed something else: For the first time in thirty years, she had had no migraine headaches!

Carol's story is consistent with the well-documented association between migraine and adverse childhood events. The prompt cessation of her headaches after gaining awareness of emotions that were repressed long ago strongly suggests that this association can exist even in the absence of overt emotional consequences. This link is frequently unsuspected, both because childhood history is often overlooked, and because of the absence of overt psychological effects of prior adversity as a consequence of the protective gift of repression.

One final interesting point about migraine concerns its preventive management. Two drug classes that are effective and have been used for decades to prevent recurrences are beta-blockers and antidepressants. As discussed previously, beta-blockers block the effects of increased sympathetic nervous system (SNS) tone; their effectiveness suggests the involvement of increased SNS tone in the pathogenesis of migraine. The recognized effectiveness of antidepressants in preventing migraine headaches, often in patients not suffering from depression or anxiety, is also suggestive of a mind-body connection linked to repressed emotions.

In many patients, migraine is a lifelong affliction that requires lifelong medication of variable efficacy. Unlike tension headaches, it generally is not associated with current stress. In this context, the documented association between migraine and a history of adverse life events, and the benefit, in some, of preventive treatment with an antidepressant or a beta-blocker, are consistent with a mind-body origin in many, one with an unsuspected link to persisting, albeit repressed emotions independent of the presence or absence of anxiety or depression. This perspective offers a new direction in understanding and treating migraine, and with it, an opportunity for both emotional healing and alleviation of migraine.

Fibromyalgia

Fibromyalgia is another example of a prevalent, yet still mysterious condition consisting of chronic, widespread pain, often accompanied by fatigue, memory problems, and sleep disturbances. It affects perhaps 2 percent of the population; it is more common in women. Fibromyalgia can begin at any age and can persist for years, seriously affecting quality of life.

Given its prevalence and its persisting and considerable impact on quality of life, fibromyalgia has been the subject of considerable medical research. Yet, here as well, as summarized in a recent review, the cause remains unknown, and tests reveal no abnormalities.[14]

Treatment can be difficult. There is no cure. Many treatment modalities have been recommended, alone or in combination, to reduce symptoms, albeit with limited effectiveness. They include stress reduction, exercise, addressing sleep problems, antidepressants, gabapentinoids, nonsteroidal anti-inflammatory drugs, opioids, and corticosteroids. Cannabinoids or low-dose naltrexone may be helpful. Three drugs, (pregabalin, duloxetine, and milnacipran), are currently FDA-approved for treatment. However, the effectiveness of treatment varies, leaving many patients with chronic pain and disability for years. In summary, we still lack a clear path to understanding and treatment of this common disorder.

In this context, studies point toward the possibility of a mind-body origin. Here as well, a meta-analysis of studies reported that patients with fibromyalgia were two to three times more likely than others to report a history of physical or sexual abuse.[15]

There is also an association between PTSD and fibromyalgia.[16] Patients with PTSD often suffer chronic pain, and patients with chronic pain are more likely to have a history of PTSD than those who are pain-free.[17] In addition, also supporting a mind-body origin is evidence of increased SNS tone in patients with fibromyalgia.[18]

Despite the evidence suggesting a mind-body connection, the possible role of repressed emotions has not been widely considered or explored. I would suspect that in many patients there is, beneath conscious awareness, a persisting burden of repressed emotions, often related to an adverse childhood history.

Supporting the possible role of repressed emotion are reports of the relevance of avoidance of negative emotions in the genesis and treatment of fibromyalgia, with benefits observed following interventions involving emotional disclosure.[19] Interestingly, analogous to my experience with patients with other disorders linked to repressed emotions, a small subset was observed to achieve a rapid and dramatic response.

These findings tell us that in a sizeable proportion of patients with a chronic pain condition that otherwise continues to defy explanation, emotions that were of necessity repressed at the time of adverse childhood events, or even events earlier in adulthood, can affect us years or decades later. Since those emotions were repressed and are inapparent to us, few suspect a link to those events. Given the lack of understanding and the disappointing results of treatment in so many patients, a new understanding linked to repressed emotions offers new pathways, both in understanding and in treating chronic, unexplained pain syndromes such as back pain, migraine, and fibromyalgia.

References

1. Lipton RB, Stewart WF, Diamond S, Diamond ML, Reed M. Prevalence and burden of migraine in the United States: data from the American Migraine Study II. Headache. 2001 Jul-Aug;41(7):646-57. doi: 10.1046/j.1526-4610.2001.041007646.x. PMID: 11554952.

2. Loder S, Sheikh HU, Loder E. The prevalence, burden, and treatment of severe, frequent, and migraine headaches in US minority populations: statistics from National Survey studies. Headache. 2015 Feb;55(2):214-28. doi: 10.1111/head.12506. Epub 2015 Feb 3. PMID: 25644596.

3. Hamelsky SW, Lipton RB. Psychiatric comorbidity of migraine. Headache. 2006 Oct;46(9):1327-33. doi: 10.1111/j.1526-4610.2006.00576.x. PMID: 17040330.

4. Radat F. What is the link between migraine and psychiatric disorders? From epidemiology to therapeutics. Rev Neurol (Paris). 2021 Sep;177(7):821-826. doi: 10.1016/j.neurol.2021.07.007. Epub 2021 Jul 27. PMID: 34325915.

5. Anda R, Tietjen G, Schulman E, Felitti V, Croft J. Adverse childhood experiences and frequent headaches in adults. Headache. 2010 Oct;50(9):1473-81. doi: 10.1111/j.1526-4610.2010.01756.x. PMID: 20958295.

6. Goodwin RD, Hoven CW, Murison R, Hotopf M. Association between childhood physical abuse and gastrointestinal disorders and migraine in adulthood. Am J Public Health. 2003 Jul;93(7):1065-7. doi: 10.2105/ajph.93.7.1065. PMID: 12835180; PMCID: PMC1447904.

7. Brennenstuhl S, Fuller-Thomson E. The Painful Legacy of Childhood Violence: Migraine Headaches Among Adult Survivors of Adverse Childhood Experiences. Headache. 2015 Jul-Aug;55(7):973-83. doi: 10.1111/head.12614. Epub 2015 Jun 23. PMID: 26104222.

8. Romans S, Belaise C, Martin J, Morris E, Raffi A. Childhood abuse and later medical disorders in women. An epidemiological study. Psychother Psychosom. 2002 May-Jun;71(3):141-50. doi: 10.1159/000056281. PMID: 12021556.

9. Tietjen GE, Brandes JL, Peterlin BL, Eloff A, Dafer RM, Stein MR, Drexler E, Martin VT, Hutchinson S, Aurora SK, Recober A, Herial NA, Utley C, White L, Khuder SA. Childhood maltreatment and migraine (part III). Association with comorbid pain conditions. Headache. 2010 Jan;50(1):42-51. doi: 10.1111/j.1526-4610.2009.01558.x. Epub 2009 Oct 21. PMID: 19845780.

10. Wegman HL, Stetler C. A meta-analytic review of the effects of childhood abuse on medical outcomes in adulthood. Psychosom Med. 2009 Oct;71(8):805-12. doi: 10.1097/PSY.0b013e3181bb2b46. Epub 2009 Sep 24. PMID: 19779142.

11. Tietjen GE, Brandes JL, Peterlin BL, Eloff A, Dafer RM, Stein MR, Drexler E, Martin VT, Hutchinson S, Aurora SK, Recober A, Herial NA, Utley C, White L, Khuder SA. Childhood maltreatment and migraine (part II). Emotional abuse as a risk factor for headache chronification. Headache. 2010 Jan;50(1):32-41. doi: 10.1111/j.1526-4610.2009.01557.x. Epub 2009 Oct 21. PMID: 19845781.

12. Sumanen M, Rantala A, Sillanmäki LH, Mattila KJ. Childhood adversities experienced by working-age migraine patients. J Psychosom Res. 2007 Feb;62(2):139-43. doi: 10.1016/j.jpsychores.2006.08.010. PMID: 17270571.

13. Tietjen GE, Khubchandani J, Herial NA, Shah K. Adverse childhood experiences are associated with migraine and vascular biomarkers. Headache. 2012 Jun;52(6):920-9. doi: 10.1111/j.1526-4610.2012.02165.x. Epub 2012 Apr 25. PMID: 22533684.

14. Bair MJ, Krebs EE. Fibromyalgia. Ann Intern Med. 2020 Mar 3;172(5):ITC33-ITC48. doi: 10.7326/AITC202003030. PMID: 32120395.

15. Häuser W, Kosseva M, Üceyler N, Klose P, Sommer C. Emotional, physical, and sexual abuse in fibromyalgia syndrome: a systematic review with meta-analysis. Arthritis Care Res (Hoboken). 2011 Jun;63(6):808-20. doi: 10.1002/acr.20328. PMID: 20722042.

16. Afari N, Ahumada SM, Wright LJ, Mostoufi S, Golnari G, Reis V, Cuneo JG. Psychological trauma and functional somatic syndromes: a systematic review and meta-analysis. Psychosom Med. 2014 Jan;76(1):2-11.

doi: 10.1097/PSY.0000000000000010. Epub 2013 Dec 12. PMID: 24336429; PMCID: PMC3894419.

17. Asmundson GJ, Coons MJ, Taylor S, Katz J. PTSD and the experience of pain: research and clinical implications of shared vulnerability and mutual maintenance models. Can J Psychiatry. 2002 Dec;47(10):930-7. doi: 10.1177/070674370204701004. PMID: 12553128.

18. Meeus M, Goubert D, De Backer F, Struyf F, Hermans L, Coppieters I, De Wandele I, Da Silva H, Calders P. Heart rate variability in patients with fibromyalgia and patients with chronic fatigue syndrome: a systematic review. Semin Arthritis Rheum. 2013 Oct;43(2):279-87. doi: 10.1016/j.semarthrit.2013.03.004. Epub 2013 Jul 6. PMID: 23838093.

19. Lumley MA, Sklar ER, Carty JN. Emotional disclosure interventions for chronic pain: from the laboratory to the clinic. Transl Behav Med. 2012 Mar;2(1):73-81. doi: 10.1007/s13142-011-0085-4. PMID: 22905067; PMCID: PMC3419371.

Chapter 14

Autoimmune Diseases

S*everal prevalent medical conditions* are considered autoimmune diseases, driven by the body's inflammatory reaction
against the self. Table 1 presents an abbreviated list of some of the
more widely recognized conditions.

Table 1: Prevalent autoimmune diseases

Crohn's disease	Temporal arteritis
Thyroiditis *(e.g., Graves disease,* *Hashimoto's thyroiditis)*	Multiple sclerosis
Psoriatic arthritis	Rheumatoid arthritis
Sarcoidosis	Scleroderma
Sjögren's Syndrome	Systemic lupus erythematosus *(SLE)*
Takayasu's arteritis	Ulcerative colitis

By definition, autoimmune diseases are mediated by an immune reaction against the self. To this day, despite decades of research, the trigger for autoimmune inflammatory reaction remains unknown. Autoimmune conditions are often treated with anti-inflammatory drugs and immunosuppressants. Although responses vary, adverse effects are common, and treatment often must be continued indefinitely.

In Chapter 11, I discussed the role of repressed emotions in inflammatory bowel disease. In this chapter I discuss evidence that suggests consideration of repressed emotions as a factor in the genesis of other autoimmune conditions as well.

⸻

Sonya, now 40, has had lupus since she was 16. She has had one major problem after another, with many hospitalizations, medications and their side effects, reduced kidney function, and other issues. She weighed 105 pounds, and recently, due to medication side effects, had lost 12 pounds.

Whenever Sonya came to see me, she was cheerful; she exuded a positive attitude. I commented about how much she had been through, and how wonderful her spirit was. She described herself as having responded that way since childhood, when she was taught to be that way.

Sonia's lupus had struck at 16. If there was a possible mind-body connection, it would have to be related to circumstances prior to that age. In response to my questions, Sonia described her father as having been strict, tough, and at times abusive, both verbally and physically. She described her mother as a cold woman.

In this touchy-feely era, we are taught to feel our emotions, to communicate them, to get them off our chest. Sonya, doing none of that, was cheerful and functioning with an incredible amount of energy despite her serious ailments.

How did she acquire the ability to not feel distressed, in a life that would have been severely distressing to almost anyone, given her childhood history and the years of illness throughout adulthood? Sonia clearly did not acquire her optimism and cheerfulness from emotionally supportive parents. Perhaps there was someone else in her childhood from whom she drew strength. Or perhaps it was genetics or faith.

However, her story suggests that she was protected by a repressive coping style, the ability to not feel the distress that could easily have overwhelmed her. Even now, with the stress of her severe and chronic illness, it would have been perfectly understandable if she had felt depressed. Yet depression had never crossed her path.

The etiology of autoimmune diseases is considered multifactorial, related to genetic, environmental, hormonal, and immunological factors. Mind-body research has examined the question of whether autoimmune diseases are linked to emotional stress. Chronic stress has been linked to autoimmune disorders including Crohn's disease, ulcerative colitis, ankylosing spondylitis, lupus, rheumatoid arthritis, and psoriasis.[1] Interestingly, perceived emotional distress, such as anxiety and depression, has not been found to be related to the development of lupus.[2] Illustrative of this, emotional distress was simply not a part of how Sonia was living her life.

A link between autoimmune conditions and repressed emotions has not yet been considered. Could a huge burden of repressed emotions, though not consciously felt, be a factor in the development of autoimmune disease, and in Sonia's case, a disease that struck her at age 16? Several findings indirectly support this understanding.

Here again, studies have demonstrated a link between adverse childhood experiences and the prevalence of autoimmune disease in adults.[3,4] A history of traumatic stress during childhood was also associated with a 70 percent increase in the likelihood of hospitalization of adult patients with autoimmune conditions.[3] Childhood maltreatment is also associated with elevation in adulthood of a widely studied marker of inflammation, C-reactive protein (CRP).[5]

There is also evidence of a link between stress-related disorders, particularly PTSD, and the development of autoimmune diseases.[1,6] Interestingly, data suggest that treatment of PTSD with an antidepressant is associated with a reduced likelihood of developing an autoimmune disorder.[1]

Also suggesting a link to emotions are studies that have observed sympathetic (SNS) and parasympathetic (vagal) nervous system dysfunction to be much more prevalent in patients with lupus, rheumatoid arthritis, and other autoimmune conditions than in a control group.[7] Studies report an increase in SNS tone and, reciprocally, a decrease in parasympathetic (vagal) tone in patients with autoimmune diseases such as lupus and rheumatoid arthritis.[8-10] These changes have also been found to play a role in mediating and dampening inflammation, as they are associated with increased blood levels of the mediators of inflammation in autoimmune disease.[11,12] And vagal nerve activation has been shown to decrease inflammatory mediators including tumor necrosis factor-α, interleukin-1

(IL-1), and IL-6, and to increase the level of the anti-inflammatory cytokine IL-10.[12]

Crucially, these findings lead to the question: Could vagal nerve stimulation offer an alternative, non-pharmacological intervention in the treatment of autoimmune disorders? Vagal nerve stimulation has been shown to inhibit the production of inflammatory cytokines including tumor necrosis factor, IL-1beta and IL-6.[12-14] Even more exciting, recent studies demonstrate its possible effectiveness in reducing inflammation and enabling clinical improvement in patients with autoimmune conditions such as rheumatoid arthritis, lupus, psoriatic arthritis and ankylosing spondylitis.[12,13,15,16]

In summary, mind-body research has failed to identify a link between autoimmune disorders and emotional distress. The observed link to childhood trauma, the abnormalities in autonomic nervous system function analogous to those associated with stress reactions, and the promising results seen with vagal nerve stimulation provide hints, though not direct proof, of the involvement in some patients of emotional factors other than emotional distress.

Here, too, the findings suggest the need to examine these new avenues for understanding the origin of, and seeking new treatment approaches for, these hard-to-treat, chronic disorders.

References

1. Song H, Fang F, Tomasson G, et al. Association of Stress-Related Disorders With Subsequent Autoimmune Disease. JAMA. 2018 Jun 19;319(23):2388-2400. doi: 10.1001/jama.2018.7028. PMID: 29922828; PMCID: PMC6583688.

2. Kwan A, Katz P, Touma Z. The Assessment of Anxiety and Depression and its Associated Factors in SLE. Curr Rheumatol Rev. 2019;15(2):90-98. doi: 10.2174/1573397114666180926101513. PMID: 30255761.

3. Dube SR, Fairweather D, Pearson WS, Felitti VJ, Anda RF, Croft JB. Cumulative childhood stress and autoimmune diseases in adults. Psychosom Med. 2009 Feb;71(2):243-50. doi: 10.1097/PSY.0b013e3181907888. Epub 2009 Feb 2. PMID: 19188532; PMCID: PMC3318917.

4. Wegman HL, Stetler C. A meta-analytic review of the effects of childhood abuse on medical outcomes in adulthood. Psychosom Med. 2009 Oct;71(8):805-12. doi: 10.1097/PSY.0b013e3181bb2b46. Epub 2009 Sep 24. PMID: 19779142.

5. Danese A, Pariante CM, Caspi A, Taylor A, Poulton R. Childhood maltreatment predicts adult inflammation in a life-course study. Proc Natl Acad Sci U S A. 2007 Jan 23;104(4):1319-24. doi: 10.1073/pnas.0610362104. Epub 2007 Jan 17. PMID: 17229839; PMCID: PMC1783123.

6. O'Donovan A, Cohen BE, Seal KH, et al. Elevated risk for autoimmune disorders in iraq and afghanistan veterans with posttraumatic stress disorder. Biol Psychiatry. 2015 Feb 15;77(4):365-74. doi: 10.1016/j.biopsych.2014.06.015. Epub 2014 Jun 28. PMID: 25104173; PMCID: PMC4277929.

7. Stojanovich L, Milovanovich B, de Luka SR, et al. Cardiovascular autonomic dysfunction in systemic lupus, rheumatoid arthritis, primary Sjögren syndrome and other autoimmune diseases. Lupus. 2007;16(3):181-5. doi: 10.1177/0961203306076223. PMID: 17432103.

8. Adlan AM, Lip GYH, Paton JFR, Kitas GD, Fisher JP. Autonomic function and rheumatoid arthritis: a systematic review. Semin Arthritis Rheum. 2014 Dec;44(3):283-304. doi: 10.1016/j.semarthrit.2014.06.003. Epub 2014 Jul 22. PMID: 25151910.

9. Adlan AM, Paton JFR, Lip GYH, Kitas GD, Fisher JP. Increased sympathetic nerve activity and reduced cardiac baroreflex sensitivity in rheumatoid arthritis. J Physiol. 2017 Feb 1;595(3):967-981. doi:

10.1113/JP272944. Epub 2016 Oct 24. PMID: 27561790; PMCID: PMC5285627.

10. Capellino S, Lowin T, Angele P, Falk W, Grifka J, Straub RH. Increased chromogranin A levels indicate sympathetic hyperactivity in patients with rheumatoid arthritis and systemic lupus erythematosus. J Rheumatol. 2008 Jan;35(1):91-9. Epub 2007 Dec 1. PMID: 18061980.

11. Ramirez-Villafaña M, Saldaña-Cruz AM, Aceves-Aceves JA, et al. Serum Neuropeptide Y Levels Are Associated with TNF-α Levels and Disease Activity in Rheumatoid Arthritis. J Immunol Res. 2020 Apr 16;2020:8982163. doi: 10.1155/2020/8982163. eCollection 2020. PMID: 32377539; PMCID: PMC7182972.

12. Rasmussen SE, Pfeiffer-Jensen M, Drewes AM, et al. Vagal influences in rheumatoid arthritis. Scand J Rheumatol. 2018 Jan;47(1):1-11. doi: 10.1080/03009742.2017.1314001. Epub 2017 Aug 2. PMID: 28766392.

13. Koopman FA, Chavan SS, Miljko S, et al. Vagus nerve stimulation inhibits cytokine production and attenuates disease severity in rheumatoid arthritis. Proc Natl Acad Sci U S A. 2016 Jul 19;113(29):8284-9. doi: 10.1073/pnas.1605635113. Epub 2016 Jul 5. PMID: 27382171; PMCID: PMC4961187.

14. Koopman FA, van Maanen MA, Vervoordeldonk MJ, Tak PP. Balancing the autonomic nervous system to reduce inflammation in rheumatoid arthritis. J Intern Med. 2017 Jul;282(1):64-75. doi: 10.1111/joim.12626. Epub 2017 May 26. PMID: 28547815.

15. Brock C, Rasmussen SE, Drewes AM, et al. Vagal Nerve Stimulation-Modulation of the Anti-Inflammatory Response and Clinical Outcome in Psoriatic Arthritis or Ankylosing Spondylitis. Mediators Inflamm. 2021 May 27;2021:9933532. doi: 10.1155/2021/9933532. eCollection 2021. PMID: 34135691; PMCID: PMC8175141.

16. Aranow C, Atish-Fregoso Y, Lesser M, et al. Transcutaneous auricular vagus nerve stimulation reduces pain and fatigue in patients with systemic lupus erythematosus: a randomised, double-blind, sham-controlled pilot trial. Ann Rheum Dis. 2021 Feb;80(2):203-208. doi: 10.1136/annrheumdis-2020-217872. Epub 2020 Nov 3. Erratum in: Ann Rheum Dis. 2021 May;80(5):e82. PMID: 33144299.

Chapter 15

Unexplained Anxiety
Unrecognized Clues from the Past

E*very physician encounters patients* who suffer from anxiety. Its two most common forms are either a seemingly lifelong history of anxiety, often labeled "generalized anxiety disorder," or anxiety related to a specific stressful situation, called "situational anxiety."

Often, generalized anxiety disorder dates to childhood. Nearly every patient I see with this disorder acknowledges having a parent who was similarly anxious. The nature/nurture question is whether the patient inherited the same gene as the anxious parent or developed anxiety after living the crucial childhood years with an anxious parent—or a combination of the two. Regardless, anxiety remains an enduring pattern that can significantly affect quality of life.

Situational anxiety occurs during a rough patch in life. The anxiety has a clear cause; its origin is not a mystery. Of course, some people experience greater anxiety than others. A supportive partner, a good hug, faith, a pill, a drink, and many other factors can help us tolerate our anxiety until the stressful situation ends.

However, I occasionally observe a third type of anxiety, one less widely discussed. It is the unexplained new onset of persisting anxiety in someone not previously troubled by anxiety, occurring when life is not particularly stressful. Patients are baffled. Why are they are feeling so anxious? It's as if the anxiety was suddenly turned on for no reason and they cannot turn it off. Their anxiety affects them greatly and begs for an explanation.

The Story of an Immigrant

Josef, 38, had three problems that had begun abruptly and that he had endured for five years: hypertension, anxiety, and a racing heart. He had been to five cardiologists and was taking five blood pressure medications. Despite the medications, from which he experienced side effects, his blood pressure had remained elevated. His heart rate frequently ran about 100 beats per minute. He felt anxious all day, every day, which felt strange to him because he had always felt calm.

As discussed earlier, one of the first steps I take in selecting medication for hypertension is deciding whether it is driven by the kidneys (as it is in 80 to 90 percent of patients with hypertension), or by the sympathetic nervous system (SNS), whose activation is commonly linked to emotion. In Josef's case, the decision was simple: His severe, persistent anxiety and rapid heart rate pointed squarely to the SNS. The question was why? Why was he so emotionally wrought?

Current stress could not explain it. Josef was an engineer and described the usual amount of ordinary work stress. His family was well. Nothing had occurred five years earlier that could explain the onset of his anxiety.

I asked about Josef's past. Had he experienced trauma during childhood? Had he been through a period of extreme life stress when severe anxiety could have been expected but was not experienced—a time when repressing that emotional distress would have protected him from feeling overwhelmed?

Nothing stood out from Josef's childhood. What about his adult life?

Josef immigrated to the U.S. at 18 from what was then Czechoslovakia. America was a foreign country; he didn't know the language, had no money, and didn't know what he was going to do.

He learned English. He studied and attended college. He supported himself by working during college and graduate school. Eventually, he achieved a successful career, marriage, and family.

Josef's is the success story of a courageous immigrant. Fortunately, at a time when the future was a complete unknown, he was not plagued by anxiety that could have plagued him for years, and could have been overwhelming. Hearing his story, the anxiety he was feeling now seemed to me to fit, hand in glove, with that earlier period in his life.

I conveyed these thoughts to him. No, he could not understand my point. Yes, he said, he had felt a "little" anxious then, but he could not grasp the possibility that he had likely, and fortunately, without conscious awareness or effort, repressed the severe, relentless, and years-long anxiety that could have been expected to occur and could have been intolerable. The suggestion that repression might have enabled him to get through the roughest time in his life and to thrive did not resonate with him.

Suspecting that Josef's hypertension was driven by the SNS, I prescribed a beta-blocker to lower his blood pressure and heart rate, and, to some extent, reduce his anxiety by blocking the effects of excessive adrenaline secretion. The medication worked.

I suspect that repression has been a vital part of resilience, not just for Josef, but for many, many immigrants. Yes, they are tough. They have to be. And in many, repression of severe or prolonged anxiety would seem to be an unrecognized but key contributor to that toughness.

Though Josef has no alternative explanation for his current anxiety, he still cannot see it as linked to the challenges of the past. His story is not dissimilar to those of some of the other resilient, and ultimately successful, immigrants I've treated. Listening to patients, I realized more and more that the explanation for their current unexplained anxiety could be found in stories they considered irrelevant to the present. Only some grasp the concept that we harbor emotions from the past that we didn't feel at that time, and that those emotions can underlie our unexplained anxiety today. Or that their resilience then was attributable to the miracle of our endowed ability, without realizing it, to repress emotions that could have devastated us.

Maureen, 38, who resided on Long Island, was referred to me concerning a recent onset of severe hypertension. Previously, her blood pressure had been normal. Amlodipine (Norvasc), a calcium channel blocker, had been prescribed but had been ineffective.

Something other than Maureen's blood pressure struck me: her tenseness and anxiety. Her heart rate was rapid at 100 beats a minute. I asked if she'd had a long-standing problem with anxiety. No, this was recent. She had always been a very calm person.

I, of course, asked about current stress. Maureen was married, and had a six-year-old daughter. She loved her job. Her marriage was fine. There was no major stress. Yet here she was, a calm person, struggling with unexplained anxiety along with unexplained elevation of her blood pressure and heart rate.

I again anticipated an unsuspected explanation linking the anxiety to events in the past, with repression of emotions that at that time could have been overwhelming.

I asked Maureen about her childhood. Good parents. No trauma or abuse. Nothing there. Even so, I suspected there had to be an origin somewhere.

Sometimes, before delving into psychosocial history, the answer pops up in the medical history. In Maureen's case, the answer became apparent when I asked the obligatory question about prior hospitalizations. She said she had been hospitalized during her pregnancy six years earlier.

The pregnancy had been problematic. She was hospitalized at the sixteenth week and remained in a hospital bed for three months. After just twenty-eight weeks of the pregnancy, it was felt necessary to deliver the baby. The baby, so critically premature, remained in a neonatal ICU for two months, during which Maureen commuted to the hospital to visit her.

Fortunately, that baby was now a normal, healthy six-year-old.

I asked Maureen about her emotional state during that five-month-long nightmare. She said she had been okay. She had been calm.

Maureen's pregnancy had been a horror. She could have been overwhelmed by relentless, prolonged anxiety occurring at a time when she could not know the outcome. That relentless anxiety could have been unbearable. Yet she'd remained amazingly calm—but not because she was doing relaxation techniques or seeing a psychotherapist or taking pills. The emotions were likely kept from her awareness by the gift of repression when there was no action she could take to relieve the prolonged stress, and when she would have been at great risk of being overwhelmed emotionally.

I offered her this explanation. I suggested that the severe anxiety she felt now, which made no sense, would have made perfect sense had she felt it then. Her resilience then had been anchored by, and required, repression of her anxiety; it had enabled her to get through those terrifying months.

Maureen understood. Immediately.

She started crying.

Maureen's toughness during that ordeal was clear. Experiencing that emotion now, with that understanding, offered an opportunity for healing—by consciously confronting that burden of emotion.

I offered Maureen a prescription for a small supply of the anxio-lytic drug, alprazolam (Xanax) to keep in her pocketbook. "It's there if you need it."

I also replaced the amlodipine with an alpha- and beta-blocker, targeting the SNS, to reduce her heart rate and blood pressure.

Maureen understood. Two weeks later, she felt better, and hadn't used the Xanax. Her blood pressure was normal.

Maureen still had to deal with a legacy of considerable, unfelt anxiety. It would likely surface again. But at least its origin appeared clear. Confronting that emotion might be a difficult task. Hopefully, understanding its origin will help in confronting it, and healing.

Maureen's story is not a rarity. Again, in my experience, when severe anxiety appears with no apparent cause, almost always, a few questions reveal a history of a severe or prolonged crisis during which the anxiety the patient was experiencing *now* would have made perfect sense—had it been felt *then*. Anxiety that had it been felt *then*, when it was unknown how or when the crisis would end, could have been overwhelming.

The absence of anxiety during the earlier crisis was enabled by the gift of repression. However, those emotions persist beneath our awareness, and eventually can cross the barrier of aware-ness. The anxiety makes no sense unless we can realize its link to the past.

There *is* a choice—to continue suffering unexplained anxiety and rely on anti-anxiety or anti-depressant medication or to rec-ognize its origin in the past, and embrace the emotions and the gift of resilience that had protected us.

And, crucial to healing, is the understanding that feeling that emotion now does not mean that we are falling apart. Having survived the crisis, now, when our life is in order, we can trust our ability to experience the long held-in emotions, and heal. And to recognize the gift of our innate ability, without conscious effort or awareness, to have shut off those emotions when we desperately needed to.

During severely stressful times, when we cannot know what the outcome will be, we *can* and do feel and tolerate anxiety and fear. But hopefully, the most severe, potentially overwhelming distress is kept from our awareness through repression. We don't realize the role repression played in tamping down, when needed, the severity of our emotional distress or that those emotions still linger within, hidden from our awareness. We might or might not eventually experience those emotions at some point in the future. And usually, if we do, we don't recognize their origin, though that recognition can be the key to understanding—and healing.

Fortunately, as in Josef's and Maureen's cases, this form of anxiety often occurs when our life is more settled, and it offers an opportunity to heal.

If, however, our current life is stressful or unstable, could the experiencing of previously repressed emotions compound our emotional distress? I suspect yes, although we would likely readily attribute our distress entirely to the current challenges.

Another question that arises: Why is our long-standing repression failing now? Is the unexplained anxiety attributable to weakening of the barrier of repression that might occur with time or age? Or is it the wisdom of our unconscious mind seeking to restore a calmer inner equilibrium by allowing our conscious mind to finally process those emotions and move on? Or both? I don't know the answer. This and many other questions are ripe for exploration once the role of repression in our lives is brought into more widespread consideration.

Happily, an understanding of unexplained anxiety offers a range of interventions. Some patients will "get" it quickly and open the door to healing. Gaining awareness is, of course, easier with stability in one's current life and with the availability of emotional support. Others might not experience the breakthrough, and will continue to view the anxiety as both problematic and unexplained.

I believe some readers will also "get" it—recognize the powerful connection of their current anxiety with their earlier history, recognize the gift of their resilience at that horrible time, and see the opportunity for healing, one facilitated by understanding that experiencing those emotions does not indicate a breakdown. This understanding is crucial to allow and tolerate the emotions that then arise.

In those unable to see a connection between their anxiety and a history of prolonged, severe stress, the widely available treatment options of an anxiolytic agent or an antidepressant, though not the optimal solution, can be extremely helpful and are important means of intervention. Another alternative, one not often considered, and which has not been adequately studied, is a beta-blocker, a medication that antagonizes the effects of oversecretion of adrenaline resulting from stimulation of the SNS. Its benefit in this regard was recognized long ago in the use of propranolol (Inderal) to prevent stage fright. A beta-blocker will reduce heart rate and blood pressure, and, crucially, can reduce anxiety and the need for psychotropic medications. For patients whose anxiety is accompanied by otherwise unexplained blood pressure elevation, including a beta-blocker in the treatment of the hypertension makes sense and is often helpful.

To sum up, patients have taught me that when marked emotional distress doesn't fit with current circumstances, the distress often makes sense when considered in the context of a history in which the ability to hide those emotions from awareness, through the gift of repression, was necessary for psychological survival. It is much healthier if we can experience the emotions flooding in now, not as emotional frailty or breakdown, but as an opportunity for healing.

It is also important to be aware that the onset of unexplained anxiety is often accompanied by physical manifestations like palpitations or elevations in blood pressure, that are similarly unexplained by one's current life situation. Those manifestations also begin to make sense when understood in this context.

Too often, this understanding is not offered. The opportunity for healing in the setting of unexplained anxiety is also often missed by concerned family and friends, and by psychopharmacologists. The potential, at long last, for healing remains unseen.

Yes, many patients respond to an antidepressant. They are effective and can be nothing short of miraculous in treating unexplained anxiety and/or depression. But they might need to be taken for months, years, or indefinitely. Recognizing the source of the unexplained agitation, and recognizing the potential for healing, offers an alternative path.

Is the healing experiencing of emotions linked to prior trauma or severe stress an option for all who suffer unexplained anxiety? I suspect it is in some, but not others. In some, it might be best that overwhelming emotions remain repressed. Experience has taught me to be guided by a patient's reaction, by the nature and severity of the trauma, and by the patient's current life circumstances. Again, as a physician, I keep in mind that the patient did not come to me to explore past trauma. That decision has to be made by the patient.

The best approach probably harks back to the adage: "Listen to the patient." If the patient is making it clear that he or she does not wish to go in that direction, perhaps that pathway should not be pursued. But I believe consideration of this understanding is important, as it provides an opportunity to begin to heal.

Emotions buried long ago *can* affect us today. When we experience frightening emotions that make no sense in the present, they often have their origin in our past. With that understanding, becoming aware of those emotions and their origin offers the chance to heal. Crucially, we can tolerate those emotions better than we think we can.

PART 4

Implications of This New Understanding

Chapter 16

Emotional Healing
Opportunities and Barriers

F *ortunately, although the origin* of many medical conditions remains incompletely understood, advances in
medical science have enabled us to treat many of them. However,
current treatment often suffers from shortcomings including
adverse effects, inadequate benefit, or the need for lifelong
administration.

The Potential for Healing
Awareness and the Barriers

Decades of listening to patients and of clinical observations, along
with published research that is consistent with these observations,
strongly suggest consideration of the role played by repressed emotions in causing or contributing to many prevalent yet incompletely

understood medical conditions. And they also offer the potential for new treatment approaches. My patients have taught me that gaining awareness of repressed emotions can enable emotional and physical healing, and in some it can do so rapidly. And where awareness is not an option, pharmacologic approaches that would not otherwise be considered offer additional avenues for successful intervention.

As described in this book, the critical first steps are the recognition that we can harbor powerful, unfelt emotions that can affect us, despite our lack of awareness of them. And that those emotions can be far more powerful than the day-to-day distress that we experience and focus on. It is time to recognize that repression is a vital component of our resilience, but to recognize also that the burden of repressed emotions can adversely affect our health.

Paying attention to the unnoticed role of repressed, unfelt emotions offers potential new paths to healing in a range of medical disorders. It is my hope that this book will bring attention to the unrecognized role of repression, and open a new frontier in trying to understand and address the mind-body connection in medicine.

However, in looking at this new understanding, important questions need to be asked. Will our unconscious mind allow us to experience *now* emotions that would have overwhelmed us *then*? Do we still need the barricade against awareness that we needed then? How do we gain that awareness?

In answering these questions, it is important to recognize and consider barriers that stand in the way of a healing awareness.

Table 1: Barriers to Awareness:

Lack of awareness of the process and impact of repression and repressed emotions	The power, born of necessity, of the barrier of repression
The severity of trauma that might require maintaining repression	Current stress, instability, or lack of emotional support
Fear, conscious or unconscious, of experiencing emotions that in the past could have been overwhelming	A history of previous trauma is not proof, per se, that it is the cause of a current medical condition
The multifactorial origin of medical conditions	The paucity of data regarding healing

The most obvious barrier to gaining awareness: it would never occur to us that we harbor powerful, unfelt emotions. That is, after all, the miracle of repression. Many patients insist that there is no emotion to get in touch with.

Many patients who have coped with painful adversity by repressing intense emotion show no signs of emotional distress. Thus, most are understandably unlikely to consider a mind-body origin. They are not motivated to seek to engage emotions of which they are unaware. Thus, the patients with inadequately explained medical disorders who are *most* likely to have a mind-body issue are also the *least* likely to be aware of the disorder's mind-body origin. Neither patient nor doctor considers a link to repressed emotions.

We need to begin recognizing the phenomenon of repression, acknowledging that we can harbor painful yet unfelt emotions and that those emotions can affect us.

Another major obstacle is the power of the partition that keeps repressed emotions from conscious awareness. Even if we understand that we harbor repressed emotions, the barrier keeping those emotions from awareness is of necessity a powerful one, and, in many, is not easily undone.

Yet another factor is the severity of the past trauma. Emotions related to massive trauma were repressed for our benefit; for some, they might best be left untouched. Although gaining awareness can be healing, a survivor of trauma of the magnitude of, for example, the Holocaust, who has repressed debilitating emotion and moved on, might not seek, or be readily able, to get in touch with those emotions. Many survivors of severe trauma are doing the best they can, not despite repression, but because of it. Confronting emotions related to severe trauma may be right for some; in others, the repression must be honored.

A crucial, yet largely overlooked obstacle to healing is fear—conscious or unconscious—of experiencing the warded-off emotion that previously could have devastated us, physically or emotionally. The same fear of being overwhelmed that led to repression remains a barrier, even if the emotion could be better tolerated today when we know we survived and were able to move on.

A patient's current life circumstances are also relevant. If one's life is in disarray, it is difficult to confront painful walled-off emotions from the past. Also of great importance is the availability of connectedness and emotional support.

Another concern is that a history of trauma is not proof, per se, that it is the cause of a current medical condition. Clearly, many medical conditions occur independently of the presence or absence of a history of trauma or repressed emotions. A history of severe trauma and repression of emotions related to it does not prove a causative relationship with a subsequent medical condition. But there is ample evidence to suggest that in many instances it can be a cause or contributor.

Also, any given medical condition can be linked to repressed emotions in some patients but not others. And the proportion attributable to the burden of repressed emotions differs from condition to condition. For example, I believe repressed emotions play an important role in almost all patients with paroxysmal hypertension, and in many with severe, resistant hypertension, and in those with unexplained hypertension at a young age. I believe chronic fatigue syndrome, fibromyalgia, and other chronic pain syndromes whose cause has remained a mystery are linked to repressed emotions in many, if not most, patients. In other medical conditions, in the absence of research concerning the role of repressed emotions, the proportion is unclear. And even in conditions known to be attributable to genetic, endocrine, and other factors. the burden of repressed emotions can be an important, though unrecognized, aggravating factor.

We need to give greater consideration to the role of repressed emotions in mind-body medicine. However, we must be cautious in attribution.

Another vital question is how to facilitate a healing awareness. Unfortunately, there has been little study of methods that can help to gain awareness in the treatment of medical disorders related to repressed emotions. I am encouraged that, in some patients, merely opening the door to understanding and self-trust can enable self-healing without the need for long-term mind-body interventions.

James Pennebaker has written about the possible healing effect of "expressive writing." He asked study participants to write about past trauma and compared its effects with the effects seen in a control group that wrote about day-to-day issues. He observed a 50 percent reduction in doctor visits, again suggesting the healing power of bringing to awareness emotions that were locked inside us.[1]

In line with his experience, I have suggested a similar exercise to patients who were able to understand and consider the possible relationship between repressed emotions and their health. This could be a reassuring letter, written as if from a caring, loving parent to the child who they were, to embrace the child with the love never received. During the writing of this letter, it can evolve in any direction. Yes, this is "playing tricks with time," but repressed emotions don't know time, as anyone who has become aware of long-repressed emotions realizes. Some patients write that letter. Others don't.

Is there a role for psychotherapy in healing medical conditions? There is little published data concerning the timing and role of psychotherapy in patients with medical rather than psychological manifestations of repressed emotions. Studies have focused on trauma survivors who were motivated to seek counseling because of emotional distress. Not yet studied is the role of psychotherapy years or decades after major trauma in patients with a medical condition who are not experiencing emotional distress related to that trauma. What's more, patients who aren't experiencing psychological distress are less likely to consider or to persist with psychotherapy, especially if progress is not achieved quickly.

I believe psychotherapy can be of benefit in processing emotions that arise. I also believe that awareness of the possible role of repressed emotions, and possibly the initial experiencing of repressed emotions, can facilitate a patient's consideration of psychotherapy. Also, as illustrated in this book, a self-healing process can occur in some, even without psychotherapy.

A major barrier in treatment is the lack of research, or awareness of the need for research, concerning *how* to promote emotional healing or other treatment alternatives in patients with medical disorders linked to repressed emotions. This healing opportunity has never been on anyone's radar. It's an area that has been almost completely overlooked in mind-body research—and it needs to be studied.

All these questions beg for further consideration and study.

Repressed Emotions: Explore or Leave Alone?

A key question is whether it could be harmful to challenge the barrier to conscious awareness. Might patients be at risk of becoming distraught upon becoming aware of long-hidden emotions? Are there some for whom the protective repression is best left unchallenged? Could the discussion open a Pandora's box of emotion that cannot be closed?

My experience strongly suggests that a wall of repression that has persisted for years or decades, if still needed, will not collapse after mere words. The problem, most often, is the opposite: Even when healing awareness is possible, the emotions remain inaccessible.

In conversations with patients who never imagined that their medical condition could be linked to repressed emotions, I approach this understanding carefully. The most important initial steps are to convey the concept of repression in understandable language, and to communicate its value as a strength integral to resilience rather than an indicator of psychopathology. I reassure patients that experiencing painful emotions that arise reflects an opening to healing and is not a sign of emotional breakdown.

As a physician, I believe it is necessary to tread gently, particularly in survivors of severe trauma, in whom emotions were repressed for good reason, and to trust the wisdom of the unconscious. Experience teaches me that there is an important built-in safeguard that resides in the wisdom of the unconscious: If the powerful barrier of repression that was constructed is still needed, it will not abandon us easily. However, if our unconscious mind allows us to experience long-repressed emotions at a time of stability and support in our life, we are likely to tolerate those emotions and heal. It is my hope that this book will be helpful to readers in opening that door to understanding and healing.

I have come to rely strongly on my patients' reactions. Some quickly understand. If they can move beyond the unconscious barrier of repression, a door to healing opens. Some might understand but have difficulty traversing the barrier of repression; here psychotherapy might play an important role in approaching those emotions. Some might prefer not to explore long-dormant emotions. For others, the concept of repressed emotion simply will not resonate.

I must keep in mind that patients seeking care for a medical condition did not come to explore old trauma or to gain awareness of repressed emotions. Although I might strongly suspect that their condition is caused or exacerbated by repressed emotions, they had no such suspicion. Should a patient not gravitate to this understanding, it is probably best to focus on standard medical alternatives. But even here, as I discuss next, this understanding opens the door to options in pharmacologic treatment that would otherwise not be considered.

To sum up, the role of repressed emotions in causing or aggravating medical conditions, and the potential impact of gaining a healing awareness, constitute a new frontier. The rapid responses seen in some patients indicate without question that gaining awareness of repressed emotions can have a therapeutic effect. The role of further interventions to facilitate healing awareness needs to be studied.

Repressed Emotions and Pharmacologic Treatment

Even if gaining a therapeutic awareness of repressed emotions is not an option, identifying a link between a medical condition and repressed emotions is important in opening the door to effective pharmacologic treatment alternatives that otherwise might not be considered.

For example, identifying patients in whom hypertension is driven by repressed emotions is valuable in guiding the selection of medication, as I discuss in my book, *Hypertension and You: Old Drugs, New Drugs, and the Right Drugs for Your High Blood Pressure.*[2] In 90 percent or so of patients, hypertension is driven by the kidneys and is not a mind-body disorder. Most respond well to medications such as ACE inhibitors, angiotensin antagonists

(ARBs), diuretics, and calcium channel blockers, drugs that target renal (kidney) and vascular mechanisms of hypertension. However, among those whose hypertension is attributable to repressed emotions, the treatment must be different.

We know that the emotions we are aware of stimulate the sympathetic nervous system (SNS). The emotions we repress and are unaware of are often far more powerful and can be expected to more strongly stimulate the SNS. Though rarely considered, those emotions are often the cause of otherwise unexplained severe or hard-to-control hypertension or unexplained hypertension in young patients; they are almost always the cause of paroxysmal hypertension.

In accord with this reasoning, in patients whose life story suggests repression of emotions related to trauma, major stress, or a repressive coping style (Ch. 9), I often prescribe, usually with considerable effect, blood pressure medications directed at the SNS, usually a beta-blocker alone or in combination with an alpha-blocker. In patients with paroxysmal hypertension (Ch. 5), this combination can quickly lower blood pressure during episodes. However, it does not prevent recurrent episodes. An antidepressant remains the only class of medication shown to be effective in preventing paroxysms; its use is truly miraculous in restoring patients' lives to normal.[3,4] When prescribed, antidepressants are effective in 80 to 90 percent of patients, including those with no history of anxiety or depression.[3-5]

Crucially, studies also confirm the benefit of antidepressants in patients with inflammatory bowel disease, although their potential benefit, particularly in patients who are not depressed, has not been adequately examined (Ch. 11). Antidepressants are also known to be beneficial in treating migraine. I have observed, and studies have shown, that antidepressants are effective in patients with chronic fatigue syndrome (CFS), another condition whose origin remains an enigma and for which treatment remains tragically inadequate. Here as well, the use of antidepressants has not been adequately studied, particularly in patients with CFS who are not depressed.

Unfortunately, the potential benefit of treatment with an antidepressant in patients with these and other medical conditions linked to repressed emotions is largely unstudied, again, because this route is not considered in patients with no history of anxiety or depression. What's more, many of those patients would be unwilling to try an antidepressant or to choose to participate in studies of the effect of an antidepressant. Thus, the absence of overt psychological symptoms constitutes a formidable barrier to the study and use of an antidepressant in patients with inadequately understood and treated medical conditions.

Ironically, an antidepressant, which shores up the barrier protecting us from emotional distress, can be regarded as the antithesis of "getting in touch," yet is often a wiser path than struggling to break down a powerful barrier that is unrecognized in most, and in many, difficult to traverse.

References

1. Pennebaker JW *Opening Up; the Healing Power of Expressing Emotions.* NY:Guilford Press, 2012.
2. Mann SJ. *Hypertension and You; Old Drugs, New Drugs and the Right Drugs for your High Blood Pressure.* Rowman & Littlefield, Lanham, MD, 2012.

3. Mann SJ. Severe paroxysmal hypertension (pseudopheochromocytoma): understanding the cause and treatment. Arch Intern Med. 1999 Apr 12;159(7):670-4. doi: 10.1001/archinte.159.7.670. PMID: 10218745.

4. Mann SJ, Solanki KV. The cause and treatment of paroxysmal hypertension. Current Hypertension Reports 2022 (in press).

5. Vaclavik J, Krenkova A, Kocianova E, Vaclavik T, Kamasova, M, Taborsky M (2015) 7B.04: effect of sertraline in paroxysmal hypertension. J Hypertens 33(Suppl 1):e93. https ://doi.org/10.1097/01. hjh.00004 67601 .49032 .62

Chapter 17

Putting It All Together

So what are the lessons learned from decades of talking with patients?

Until now, studies and books on the mind-body relationship have focused on the day-to-day stress we encounter and the emotional distress we feel. Traditional psychosomatic research has sought to demonstrate that many medical conditions are linked to emotional distress and that stress reduction techniques can provide effective treatment. It's time, however, to acknowledge that the impact of that large body of research on our understanding of the origin and treatment of medical conditions has been limited.

Those disappointing results ring true with my experience as a physician. Yes, the emotional distress we feel can cause functional symptoms such as headaches, fatigue, diarrhea, and others, and can raise blood pressure in the moment. Yes, it can *indirectly* cause medical illness by contributing to harmful health habits like over-eating and obesity, smoking, and alcohol and substance abuse. But the day-to-day stress we encounter and the emotional distress we feel are usually not the *direct* cause of medical conditions such as hypertension, ulcers, inflammatory bowel disease, chronic fatigue syndrome, and many others.

After decades of mind-body research, it's clear that many medical conditions are not "mind-body" disorders. For most patients, hypertension, once considered the quintessential stress-related disorder, is not a mind-body disorder. Before we can determine which conditions do have a mind-body component, and in what proportion of patients this understanding is relevant, we first need to better understand its nature. Yet we remain tied to an understanding that hasn't worked. We are essentially back at square one.

The Overlooked Power of Repression

Decades of listening to patients has taught me to pay attention to the almost entirely unexplored role of the powerful emotions we *don't* feel and we *don't* realize we harbor. The day-to-day stress we cope with and talk about is minor compared with the overwhelming stress so many experience at a certain period in their life or have cumulatively endured. It is also minor compared to the cumulative emotional burden resulting from a lifelong repressive coping style. We had to have been equipped, and, in fact, *are* equipped, with the ability to not feel, an ability that humankind badly needed to survive emotionally. We have, through the gift of repression, much more resilience than we realize. However, though unaware, we carry a burden of persisting, albeit repressed, emotions.

Repression does not provide universal resilience. It does not protect all of us all the time. Many suffer from and are overwhelmed by painful emotions that are not repressed. Repression does not shield everyone and does not shield us at all times. Nevertheless, how much worse off so many of us would be, and are, without the silent protection given us by the power of our unconscious mind to repress.

I've heard story after amazing story of emotional survival. The resilience shown in the stories of my patients moved me to write this book. Their stories have taught me that we are wired, consciously and unconsciously, to be resilient.

Yet the role of repression as a key component of our resilience remains overlooked. Its invisibility attests to how well the process of repression is partitioned from our awareness. We are able to repress powerful emotions without knowing we are repressing them—and we are unaware that the repression is protecting us.

We must recognize that repressing that which would have overwhelmed us is not psychopathology; it is often an unrecognized cornerstone to our emotional resilience and survival. It is a powerful gift, yet one that we don't even realize is operative. To hear a trauma survivor say, "It had no lingering emotional effect," is a testament not to rigidity or psychological blindness, but to the mysterious quality of our most powerful defense: When it is most in effect, we are least aware of it!

We don't realize that although we do experience considerable emotional pain, we also are able to repress that which we need to repress. This unnoticed gift at some point plays a role in the lives of most of us, and, along with the many other resources that support our resilience, enables us to move on from painful events, or to deal with emotions at a pace we can tolerate.

Also unrecognized is the powerful but silent effect of repressed emotions on our health. Few recognize the crucial role of repression in our resilience, and even fewer recognize its effects on our health, effects that remain under the radar of both medical science and traditional mind-body research. The burden of repressed emotions, even though we are unaware of it, can silently cause or contribute to medical or psychological sequelae that can develop decades later. This does not mean that everyone who harbors repressed trauma-related emotions will develop medical consequences. But, although largely unknown in the field of mind-body medicine, unacknowledged emotions can and do affect us.

Noticing the missing emotions in patients' stories led me to realize that long-standing repression of deeply painful emotion, though a vital gift, can also be associated with silent harm, even decades later. Patients' stories are consistent with the many studies that have documented a link between prior stress or trauma, particularly childhood events, and adult medical conditions. Many patients did not initially mention those stories. Nor at first did their stories seem relevant to their current medical issues. But those stories were not irrelevant. They often held a key to understanding.

Similarly, even in the absence of a history of trauma, a repressive coping style and the tendency to be unaware of the troubling emotions of day-to-day life, can also be associated with various medical conditions. Although a repressive coping style serves humankind in a cruel world, it also has its downside.

The purpose of this book is not to answer all the questions about repression and the mind-body link. It is to ask the questions and open the door to consideration of the role of repressed emotions in the mind-body link, and the implications of that link in understanding and treating medical illness. This understanding is particularly important because, despite all our acquired knowledge about the pathophysiology of so many disorders, we still don't understand what triggers them. And, for many, a need for more effective treatment remains. A new understanding opens the door to new treatment options.

Questions We Need to Explore

There is much that we need to learn that we haven't begun to explore: In which medical conditions do repressed, unfelt emotions play a role? In what proportion of patients with those conditions are repressed emotions contributory? How do we best identify those in whom the burden of repressed emotions is relevant to their medical condition? Can gaining awareness of repressed emotions ameliorate—and even heal—those conditions? How can we best open the door to awareness and healing?

In whom might it be best to leave repressed emotions untouched? Can gaining awareness be harmful? Crucially, does seeking and gaining awareness of previously repressed emotion, or rapidly gaining awareness following a discussion of past events, differ from unsought awareness that arises, with time and age, from weakening and failure of the wall of repression? My experience, reassuringly, suggests yes, it does differ.

Finally, if gaining awareness is not an option, can other forms of treatment based on this understanding ameliorate medical conditions linked to the burden of repressed emotions? Here, again, my experience and published studies indicate that it can. This understanding makes possible a better selection of medication in treating hypertension, and offers more effective use, even in patients who are not depressed or anxious, of antidepressants that can help bring chronic medical illnesses under improved control. But we need to better understand which patients and which medical conditions are best aligned to benefit from this understanding.

The footprint of repressed emotions in many medical conditions needs to be explored and assessed. But before it is studied, it first needs to be considered.

The goal of mind-body research is ultimately to ameliorate the burden of disease. Mind-body research has focused entirely on interventions aimed at the emotional distress patients are aware of and report. No attention has been paid to addressing the intense emotions that lie beneath conscious awareness. My patients have taught me that gaining understanding and awareness can lead to self-healing—in some, quickly. Although experiencing these emotions is painful, we can trust the wisdom of our unconscious. But to date, in understanding and treatment of medical disorders, the question of whether, how, and in whom to pursue awareness of repressed emotions has barely been raised.

Clearly, there are barriers to awareness and healing. One key barrier is fear. I believe this fear can be tempered with the realization that the unconscious barrier against awareness that has been maintained for years or decades will not collapse if it is still needed.

My experience teaches me that there is value in offering this mind-body understanding to patients and in being guided by their reaction. We must respect that the barrier of repression should not always be challenged. As previously discussed, even if emotional healing appears unlikely, this understanding nevertheless brings into consideration effective treatment alternatives.

The role of repression remains too important to continue to overlook. The logic is incredibly simple. Though rarely recognized, repression is crucial to our psychological well-being and is at the heart of our resilience. It is a gift without which humankind could not have survived emotionally through millennia of suffering. Yet we don't even realize it is operative. Equally unrecognized is that the burden of repressed emotions lingers, and more than the emotions we are aware of, it can be linked to adverse health consequences. Though unknown to most physicians, patients, and researchers, our most painful and powerful emotions are often those that were repressed, often of necessity, and hidden from our awareness. It is not illogical to suspect that those emotions, though unfelt, persist and affect us. This remains the secret of the mind-body connection; a secret that offers new paths to understanding and treatment.

It is my hope that the observations chronicled in this book and data that support these observations will help stimulate awareness, interest, and research in this area. I also hope some readers will recognize, from the stories of my patients, parallels in their own lives, and recognize the role repression has played in their life or in the life of someone close to them.

I believe this understanding can open the door to awareness and to trusting the wisdom of our unconscious mind—that in allowing those emotions into awareness, it is opening the door to healing.

Understanding the role of repressed emotions in medical illness constitutes a frontier that we have not yet even begun to explore. It is time to begin that journey.

Acknowledgments

My interest and career in hypertension would likely never have flourished without the support I have received from many people. Dr. John Laragh, a pioneer in the field of hypertension, opened the door for me to pursue the mysteries and challenges of hypertension at NewYork-Presbyterian Hospital - Weill Cornell Medical College. I have had the opportunity to share and grow this interest with my colleagues at the Hypertension Center, Drs. Phyllis August, Mark Pecker and Line Malha.

I am grateful to Cat Jennings, my publicist. And to IngramSpark for enabling writers who are not famous to publish and convey their important works. And to the technological geniuses whose inventions facilitated the ability of a non-writer to become a writer.

I am grateful for the coincidences that we did not earn or deserve that underlie so much of what we achieve in life. And to Charlie Bloom whose interaction with me on October 29, 1986 somehow, and amazingly, reset my trajectory in life.

I am grateful for the wonders of evolution that provided us with the gift of repression and so many other tools to help us withstand the life stresses that so deeply challenge all of us. And for the gift of meaningfulness that enables us to focus and persevere for years until we complete a task we were meant to perform.

I am indebted to my family, with whom I have shared this journey on earth, for their loving support during the years that my passion to write this book monopolized so much of my spare time. To my wife Maureen, my partner in life, for tolerating and loving me, and to David and Meg, with my admiration and love.

Index

About the Author

D*r. Mann is a physician*, researcher, and author. He specializes in the management of hypertension at the NewYork-Presbyterian Hospital-Weill Cornell Medical College, where he is a Professor of Clinical Medicine. He has published numerous papers in leading medicine, hypertension and psychology journals, and numerous book chapters. He has also published two previous books:

Healing Hypertension: A Revolutionary New Approach focuses on the mind-body connection in patients with hypertension.

Hypertension and You: Old Drugs, New Drugs, and the Right Drugs for Your High Blood Pressure focuses on how best to individualize and optimize hypertension drug therapy.

He has focused on the individualization of treatment for hypertension as a means of achieving blood pressure control in nearly all patients. And at a prestigious medical institution at the forefront of heart health and traditional medicine, he has been able to combine optimization of the medical treatment of hypertension with a revolutionary view concerning the mind-body connection that is reflected both in patient care and in his publications.

Made in United States
North Haven, CT
01 November 2024

59722369R00124